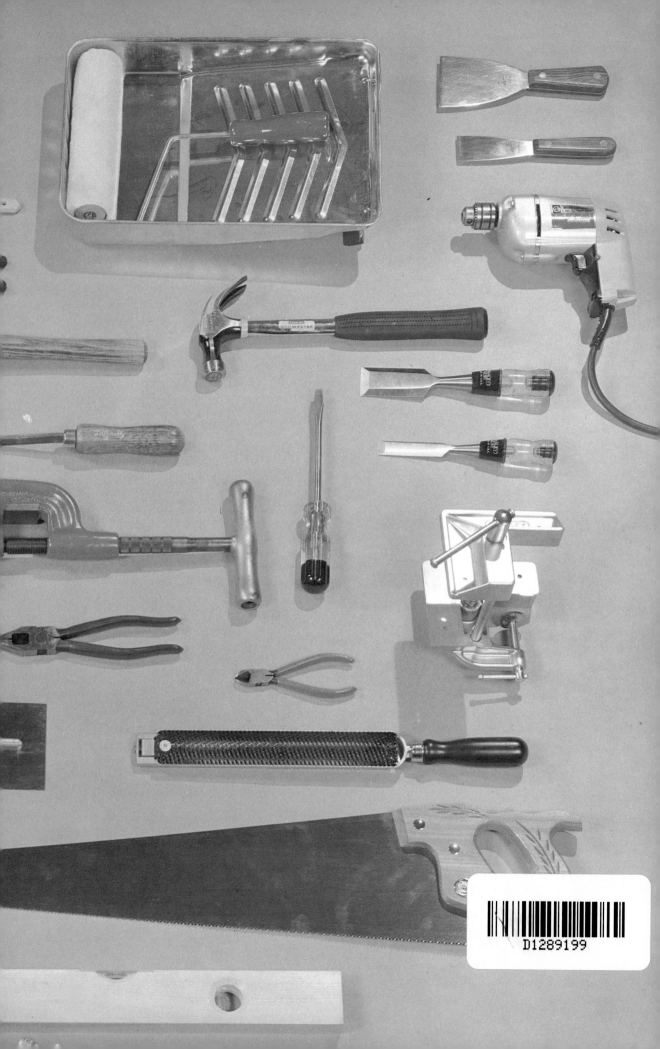

THE
PRACTICAL
HANDYMAN'S
ENCYCLOPEDIA

photograph courtesy of Armstrong Cork Co.

THE
PRACTICAL
HANDYMAN'S
ENCYCLOPEDIA

THE COMPLETE

ILLUSTRATED

DO IT YOURSELF

LIBRARY FOR HOME & OUTDOORS

VOLUME TWO

GREYSTONE PRESS/NEW YORK · TORONTO · LONDON

18668

CONTENTS OF VOLUME TWO

A Barbecue with Privacy

Utility and good looks are features of this unit which helps you keep outdoor meals "in the family."

A BARBECUE wall can make a real "outside room" of the terrace which it conceals.

A four-inch concrete slab already existed as the terrace floor in this case. An additional 1⅝ inches was poured over the area to support the barbecue, reinforced with ½-inch rods at 10-inch intervals. The form for the concrete was made of 2x4s placed flat.

If you are starting from scratch, use 2x6's for building the form. If there is any doubt about the site being well drained, excavate to a depth of ten or twelve inches and fill to within five inches of the grade with coarse, well-compacted gravel before placing form.

Preferably, make your slab 5x10 feet. This will give you ample paved area along the front of the barbecue and along its counters. It requires one cubic yard of concrete—a convenient and economical amount for transit delivery. You can, however, get by with only ½ yard of concrete by doing the following: instead of a rectangular form of 5x10 feet, make a T-shaped form measuring 2x10½ feet in its longest dimension, with the leg of the T measuring 19x46 inches. This will allow a 1-inch extension of the concrete slab on every side of the unit.

If you live in an area where frost is a factor, take warning: be sure to reinforce the slab with 6x6-inch mesh. When the concrete is poured, lift the mesh so that it is an inch or more from the bottom. Using a straightedge, level off concrete even with top of the form.

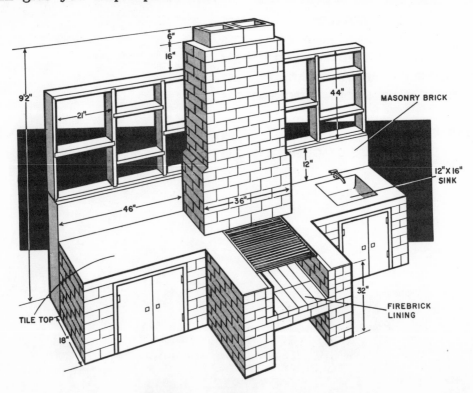

OVERALL VIEW

Materials List

650 common brick
38 firebrick
 6 8½"x13" flue tile
 1 cu. yd. concrete
 3 bags portland cement
 3 bags lime
 ½ yd. sand
 6 ½"x28" reinforcing rod
65 sq. ft. 6"x6" reinforcing mesh
 1 2"x2"x30" steel angle
 6 ½"x8" bolts with washers and nuts
 1 20"x24" grate
 1 12"x16" sink with faucet and fittings
16 linear ft. T&G cypress or redwood 1x6
60 linear ft. 2x4 redwood
 galvanized nails
60 4"x4" tiles
50 cap tiles
 Adhesive, tile grout

When the concrete has set sufficiently so that a wood trowel does not dig in, "float" the slab to an even, gritty finish, using arcing strokes. Those who are new at concrete work seem inclined to rush into the floating operation. So if you haven't worked concrete much before, be careful . . . take your time. Do *not* float until the concrete has really firmed up.

Lay up the brick walls and the masonry back wall of the barbecue simultaneously, making sure with a spirit level and rafter square that every course you lay is level, plumb and square at the corners. The bricks are to be laid on their narrow sides, except for the storage area just under the firebox. A flat course of bricks also is used as a starter course for the block wall.

All measurements shown in the accompanying sketches are approximate and can be varied somewhat to accommodate the particular size of the brick you are using.

If you want to use mortar cement, make your mortar mixture of one part cement and three parts sand. If you use conventional portland cement, make your mix one part cement to one part lime and six parts sand. After mixing the dry ingredients thoroughly, add only enough water to make the mortar a thick mud. If the mortar flows, you've added too much water.

Make your mortar joints about ⅜ inch thick, never more than ½ inch, and compact the joints with a jointing tool as soon as the mortar has begun to set. If the weather is hot and dry, it may be advisable to dampen the blocks and bricks before using them. They should never be either bone-dry or soaking wet. Fire bricks should *never* be dampened, and their joints should be on the tight side.

The section under the firebox is for storage of charcoal and other supplies. Support the brickwork above it with ½-inch reinforcing rods, 28 inches long. These will span the opening with four inches to spare on either side. Allow

two supporting rods for each brick used.

The chimney "throat" is six inches high and begins approximately six inches above the level of the firebox floor. Use a 2x2x30-inch angle to support the masonry above the throat. The brickwork forming the smoke shelf at the bottom of the chimney is made by bridging the void between the brick walls below.

The counter top is made of precast concrete slab sections 3⅝ inches thick, poured on the ground in forms made of 2x4's. Two sections measuring 18x42 inches, and two sections 7x36 inches are needed for this. Allow a cutout for the sink just large enough to permit support for the sink's flange.

After the slabs have been placed in position, set the tile top with waterproof adhesive, following the adhesive manufacturer's instructions. Adhesive is applied with a notched spreader (or a notched trowel). A dab of adhesive is placed on the back of each tile before it is set. Tiles are set down to one side of where they belong and then slid into place.

The tiles themselves are nominal 4x4-inch squares, actually measuring ¼ inch larger than that in each direction. No cutting of tiles should be necessary,

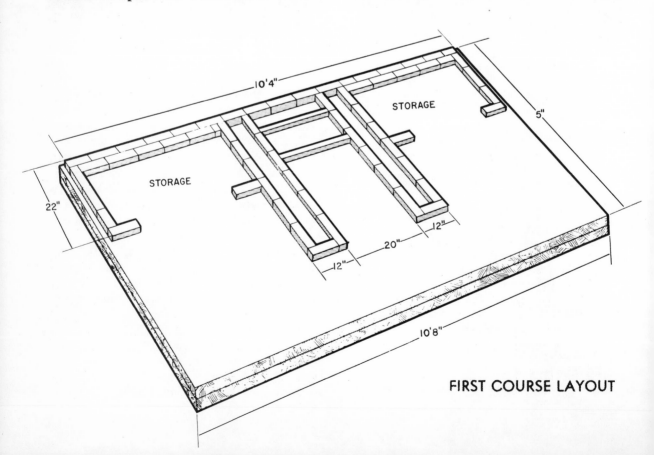

FIRST COURSE LAYOUT

but the tiles may be cut if needed. To cut them, first score along the line of the cut with a glass cutter. Then snap at the scored line after clamping the tile in a vise, or place the tile over a triangular file on the floor and step on either side to snap apart.

After the tiles have been set, brush on a pasty tile grout with a paintbrush. Tile grout can be bought in powder form from your tile supplier, or you can mix white portland cement with water to about a cake-batter consistency. Squeegee the excess cement from the tiles, and wipe with a soft cloth. When the cement has hardened, wipe the tiles clean with a damp sponge.

Six courses above the counter top, the chimney is narrowed the width of half a brick on either side. Six lengths of 8½x13-inch flue tile are needed to line the chimney. Tiles start approximately six inches above counter top level and are supported by bricks set flat, so that each projects about two inches beyond the brick just below it.

Do not attempt to put mortar in the joints between tile sections. Instead, plaster mortar well on the outside of the joints. The twin flue tiles are butted together, dry. Cap the chimney with a ½-inch topping of mortar sloped away

from the flues, keeping the flues clear.

The top course of the block wall backing the barbecue unit is filled solid with rubble and mortar and six ½x8-inch anchor bolts are inserted so they project two inches above the wall's top. The divider frame is built on the ground, made of 2x4's. For better holding power, the corner joints should be rabbeted and crosspieces set in dadoes. With holes predrilled in the bottom member to accept anchor bolts, raise the frame into position and tighten nuts.

The sink faucet may be attached to the house plumbing line, or you can get hose adapters for ½-inch copper pipe and make a hose connection to existing outside cock. In areas subjected to freezing, be sure to make provision for shutoff and draining of the line.

Sink waste may be connected to the house plumbing or to a dry well—a three-foot pit filled with rocks. Six inches below grade level, cover the rocks with tarpaper and replace the top soil. No drain tap is necessary if you are connecting to a dry well.

The doors for the storage cabinets are made of tongue-and-groove boards secured with battens. The door opening is framed with 2x4's.

—D. X. Manners

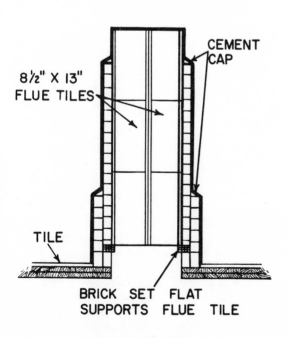

CHIMNEY SECTION

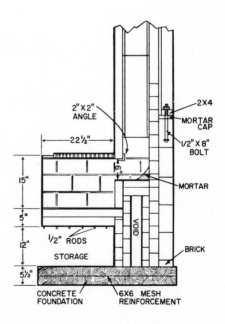

CROSS SECTION

Contemporary

Barbecue Cart

It adjusts to cooking or eating height, has spacious tray and pull-out shelf

Holes drilled in shelf will steady feet of brazier. The barbecue cart folds away for easy storage.

CUT identical pieces at one time, if possible. To cut a hand opening, as for tray, drill a hole at each end of area to be cut away; saw out excess with a compass saw. Glue all surfaces to be nailed or screwed together. Countersink screwheads.

Enlarge cart pattern (each square equals 1" square) to cut sides, handles, and legs; follow diagram to assemble. Make top of cart by piecing boards between sides and ends. Screw handles in place through top. Screw runner strips to underside for pullout shelf.

Cut shelf ¾" x 11½" x 25¼". (See photograph.) To protect end grain, nail a ¾" x 1¾" strip along each long edge. Plane shelf to slide smoothly on runners. Chisel a shallow hand grip on underside of one end. On upper surface, 15¾" from front, chisel a small groove to accommodate turn button, which will keep shelf from pulling out or slipping back. *Note:* We drilled holes in shelf to steady feet of brazier.

Screw hardwood cleats to underside of cart, following diagram. Back legs will slide between these when height of cart is changed.

Drill holes in legs following placement on pattern. Assemble front legs with 18¾" crosspiece, screwing through edges of legs into crosspiece. Drill hole in each end of axle (drill rod) for cotter pins; slip axle into place. Fit wheels over ends with a washer on each side. Fit cotter pins in holes. Bolt top of legs to handles, with a washer on each side of handle and one on inside of leg.

Assemble back legs with 17" crosspiece, below center, and hardwood crosspiece at top, planed as in pattern. Bolt leg sections together, with a washer inside, outside, and between legs. With legs in position shown in pattern, screw halves of one sash lock

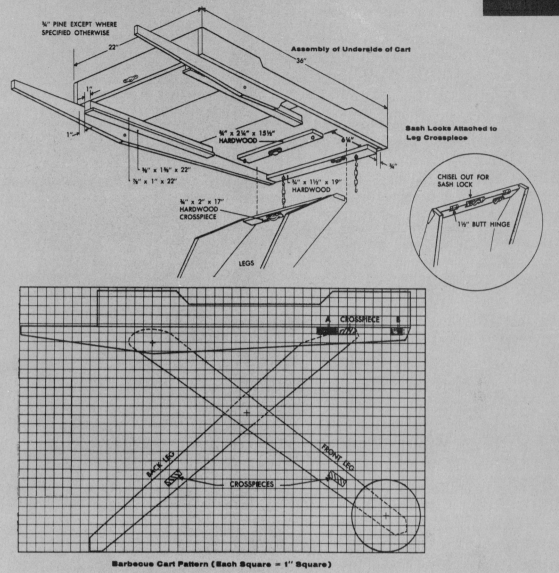

¾" PINE EXCEPT WHERE
SPECIFIED OTHERWISE

22"

Assembly of Underside of Cart

36"

1"

1"

¾" x 2¼" x 15½"
HARDWOOD

Sash Locks Attached to
Leg Crosspiece

⅜" x 1⅜" x 22"

⅞" x 1" x 22"

¾" x 1½" x 19"
HARDWOOD

¾" x 2" x 17"
HARDWOOD
CROSSPIECE

6¼"

¾"

CHISEL OUT FOR
SASH LOCK

1½" BUTT HINGE

LEGS

A   CROSSPIECE   B

BACK LEG

FRONT LEG

CROSSPIECES

Barbecue Cart Pattern (Each Square = 1" Square)

to leg crosspiece and cleat A. Move legs to fit against outer cleat B; screw halves of other sash lock to cleat B and leg crosspiece.

To keep crosspiece between cleats A and B, attach chains to screw eyes in cleats. Screw hinges to crosspiece under chains, to keep chains from wearing away wood. Insert remaining screw eye in center of crosspiece between front legs. To fold cart for storing, unhook chains from cleat A; hook onto this screw eye.

Make tray that rests on leg crosspieces from ½" lumber. (See photograph.) Finished tray is 3" high, 15" wide, and 25" long. Piece bottom for required width, and nail between sides and ends. Cut a 1" x 3½" slot for hand opening at each end. Screw ½" x ½" x 15" strips on underside to butt against crosspieces and hold tray in place.

FINISHING: Set nailheads and fill all holes with plastic wood. Sand entire piece, first with medium sandpaper, then fine. Apply a coat of stain. Apply a coat of shellac, thinned 50-50 with alcohol, then a coat of varnish. Rub down with fine steel wool after each coat. Glue sheet of aluminum into top of cart. •

Bill of Materials

⅜" x 1⅝", ½", ¾", and ⅞" x 1" pine lumber; ¾" hardwood; waterproof glue; nails; screws; 20½" x 34½" sheet of aluminum; 2 window-sash locks; two 1½" butt hinges; 2 heavy chains with S hooks at ends, 8½" long including hooks; 5 screw eyes; turn button; four 2" bolts with 3 washers and a nut to fit each; ½" drill rod, 23" long; 4 washers to fit rod; 2 cotter pins; two 1¼" x 8"-diameter rubber-tired wheels; pine stain; shellac; alcohol; spar varnish.

(Photo left) Located next to swimming pool, this barbecue is protected from weather by a solid wood overhang.

For the ultimate in outdoor living and entertainment, Louis Hochman suggests this

CHEF'S DELIGHT BARBECUE

(Photo above) Beyond barbecue is a poolside dressing room constructed of redwood.

FOR THE connoisseur of charcoal cookery, there's little to equal this super deluxe outdoor barbecue which features every modern convenience to make outdoor cooking and eating a savory delight.

Most outstanding of its features is its unique rotisserie barbecue grill which, in addition to the usual grill-type cooking facilities, also provides a vertical grill to hold the hot charcoals in a vertical bank against the back wall of the barbecue for spit roasting. With this arrangement, a large roast or fowl can be placed on a spit and rotated before the coals without any danger of its juices dropping into the fire and flaming up to scorch or burn the meat. A stainless steel baste pan is provided to catch the juices and keep them handy for basting purposes. The spit operates on a horizontal chain drive and can be dropped into any one of a number of notches in a bracket which parallels the chain to adjust the space between the meat and the fire.

For charcoal broiling of steaks, chops, and similar flat cuts, the fire is built on the floor of the barbecue pit under the horizontal grill which holds the meat. This grill can be raised or lowered above the fire by means of a rack and pinion gear mechanism which is operated by a hand crank projecting from the masonry near the barbecue opening.

The spit motor comes assembled to the chain drive mechanism and one of the notched spit brackets. This motor unit is built right into the masonry as the barbecue takes shape. It can be had for either right or left side mounting.

To conserve heat while roasting meat on a spit, the barbecue opening can be closed off with two large steel doors, and the draft can be cut down by closing a damper in the chimney. Both of these accessories come with the barbecue unit which also includes an ash dump lid and a small cast iron ash door. The rotor grill unit used in the barbecue shown, is the CB-3 Barbecue which is made and supplied by Rotor Sales of North Hollywood, Calif.

Aside from the unique barbecuing features of this outdoor unit, the barbecue also has a separate gas heated warming oven, a charcoal storage compartment, a sink, and adequate storage space under the sink.

The barbecue was designed to fit into the poolside setting of a yard landscaped by landscape architect, Warren E.

Lauesen of North Hollywood, California. It stands under a solid waterproof overhang up against a back wall and the side of a redwood dressing room.

To harmonize with the rustic redwood dressing room wall texture, the cabinet doors under the sink were made of redwood, and a small redwood cupboard shelf was built in above the sink as shown. If desired, the L-shaped design of this barbecue can be altered to a straight or V-line shape to fit your own individual requirements.

Use Common Bricks

The barbecue is built of common bricks, which measure 3x3¼x10 inches. The foundation is 12 inches thick, reinforced with steel rods; it should extend at least four inches beyond the barbecue base on all sides.

The basic measurements shown can be used as a guide in building the unit. Most important consideration: be sure that the walls and top around the warming oven chamber are at least eight inches thick. This thickness is easily achieved by laying two walls of brick together with a 1 to 1½-inch space between them filled with mortar. This mortar-filled space can be wider but should not be less. Walls, pit bottom of barbecue chamber, and chimney should also be at least eight inches thick. Do not make them any thinner.

For the 6x9-inch cast iron ash door, a masonry opening of 6½x9 inches should be provided. The fuel bin masonry opening of 17x22½ inches will accommodate a 21x17-inch steel door. The 15x17-inch masonry opening for the oven will take a 14x16-inch cast iron door.

Steel and cast iron doors may vary in

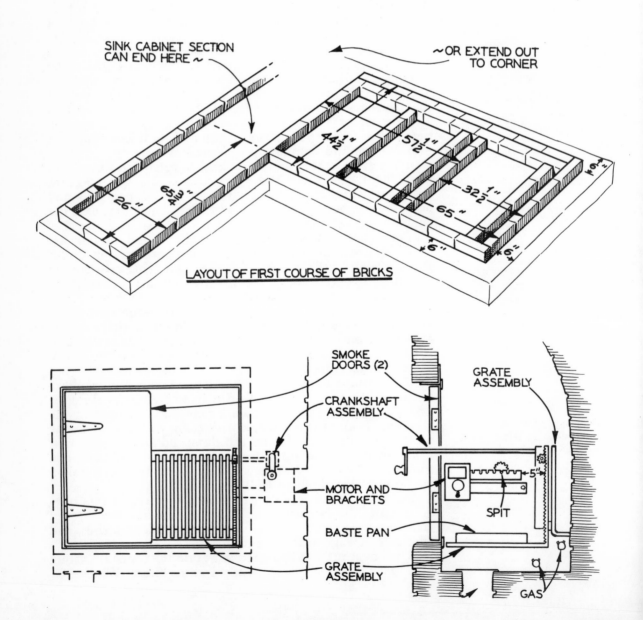

LAYOUT OF FIRST COURSE OF BRICKS

size with different manufacturers around the country so before making openings, check the door sizes available in your neighborhood, and make openings to fit them. Since all openings are covered with doors, no angle irons or lintels are needed to support the course of bricks over each opening. The door frames themselves supply this support. Set the doors into their openings as you build the walls around them.

Doors in Sink Section

The doors in the sink section are made of ⅞-inch thick redwood and set into 2x4 frames, as shown in diagram. These frames consist of three lengths of 2x4 wood, two set into the masonry opening vertically, and the third bridged across them at the top.

No frames are necessary on the bot-

tom. The two side pieces are held in place by driving long nails through them into the soft mortar. The top piece is nailed to the two vertical pieces. It is best to nail these three pieces together beforehand and then build a wall around them. The top cross piece will serve as a lintel to support the bridging course of bricks. The redwood doors should be rabbetted on all four edges, as shown, to fit into the frame opening. Wooden knobs and decorative black wrought iron hinges and catches dress up the finished doors.

To insure perfect alignment, build up all walls at the same time and use a level on each course of bricks to keep the lines straight and level. As the walls go up around the sink section, build the wooden shelf into place by nailing lengths of ¾-inch shelving across three supports made of 2x4's held securely to the wall with

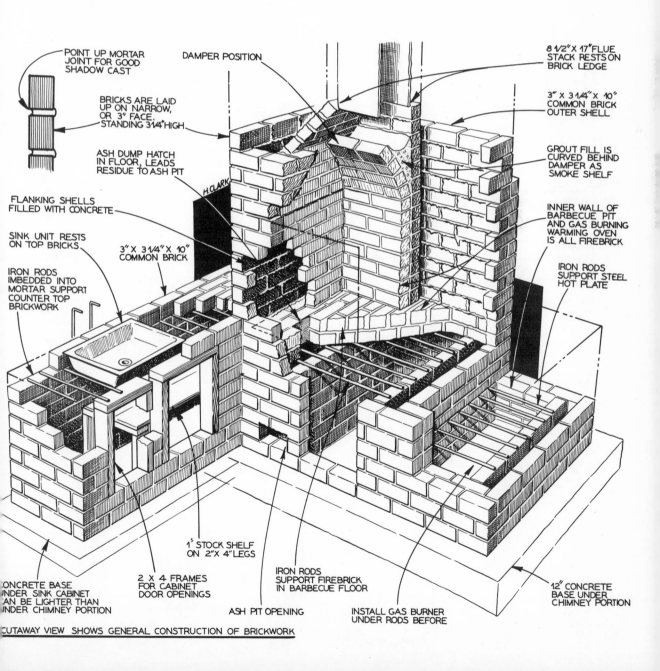

POINT UP MORTAR JOINT FOR GOOD SHADOW CAST

DAMPER POSITION

8 ½" X 17" FLUE STACK RESTS ON BRICK LEDGE

BRICKS ARE LAID UP ON NARROW, OR 3" FACE, STANDING 3¼" HIGH

3" X 3¼" X 10" COMMON BRICK OUTER SHELL

ASH DUMP HATCH IN FLOOR, LEADS RESIDUE TO ASH PIT

GROUT FILL IS CURVED BEHIND DAMPER AS SMOKE SHELF

H. CLARK

FLANKING SHELLS FILLED WITH CONCRETE

INNER WALL OF BARBECUE PIT AND GAS BURNING WARMING OVEN IS ALL FIREBRICK

SINK UNIT RESTS ON TOP BRICKS

3" X 3¼" X 10" COMMON BRICK

IRON RODS SUPPORT STEEL HOT PLATE

IRON RODS IMBEDDED INTO MORTAR SUPPORT COUNTER TOP BRICKWORK

1' STOCK SHELF ON 2" X 4" LEGS

2 X 4 FRAMES FOR CABINET DOOR OPENINGS

IRON RODS SUPPORT FIREBRICK IN BARBECUE FLOOR

12" CONCRETE BASE UNDER CHIMNEY PORTION

CONCRETE BASE UNDER SINK CABINET CAN BE LIGHTER THAN UNDER CHIMNEY PORTION

ASH PIT OPENING

INSTALL GAS BURNER UNDER RODS BEFORE

CUTAWAY VIEW SHOWS GENERAL CONSTRUCTION OF BRICKWORK

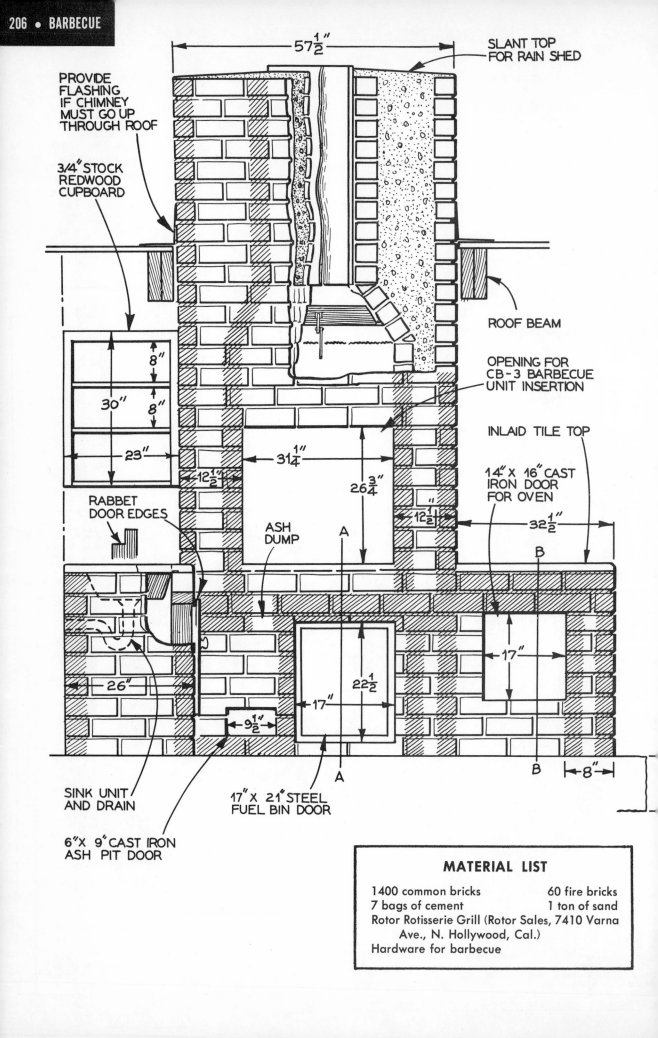

SLANT TOP
FOR RAIN SHED

57½"

PROVIDE
FLASHING
IF CHIMNEY
MUST GO UP
THROUGH ROOF

3/4" STOCK
REDWOOD
CUPBOARD

ROOF BEAM

OPENING FOR
CB-3 BARBECUE
UNIT INSERTION

INLAID TILE TOP

8"

30"

8"

23"

14" X 16" CAST
IRON DOOR
FOR OVEN

12½"

31¼"

26¾"

12½"

32½"

RABBET
DOOR EDGES

ASH
DUMP

A

B

26"

17"

17"

22½"

A

B

8"

9½"

SINK UNIT
AND DRAIN

17" X 21" STEEL
FUEL BIN DOOR

6" X 9" CAST IRON
ASH PIT DOOR

MATERIAL LIST

1400 common bricks   60 fire bricks
7 bags of cement   1 ton of sand
Rotor Rotisserie Grill (Rotor Sales, 7410 Varna
          Ave., N. Hollywood, Cal.)
Hardware for barbecue

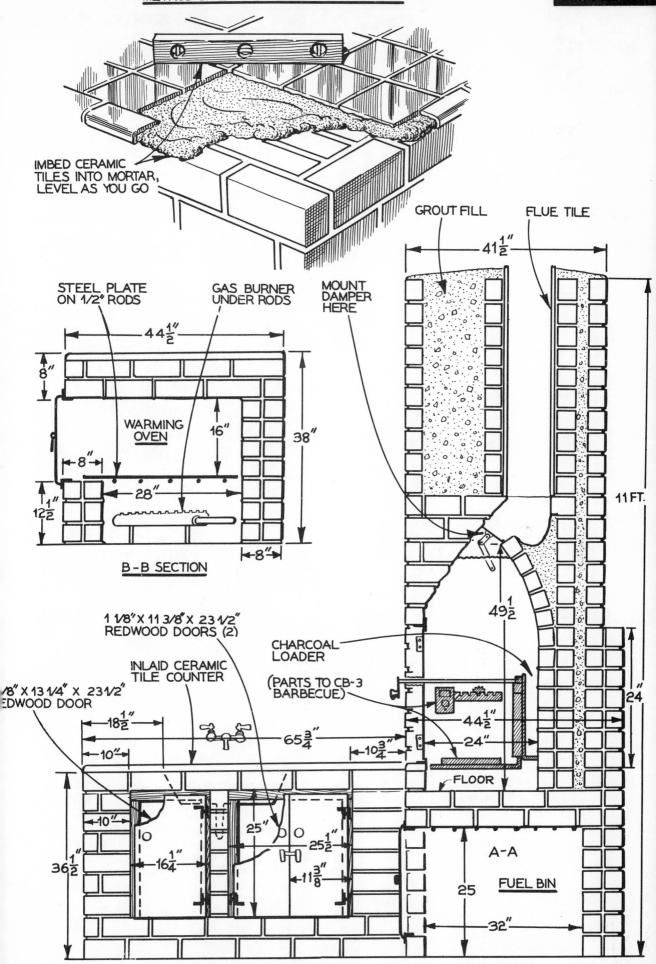

METHOD OF LAYING A TILE COUNTER TOP

IMBED CERAMIC TILES INTO MORTAR, LEVEL AS YOU GO

GROUT FILL

FLUE TILE

41 1/2"

11 FT.

STEEL PLATE ON 1/2" RODS

GAS BURNER UNDER RODS

MOUNT DAMPER HERE

44 1/2"

8"

WARMING OVEN

16"

38"

8"

28"

12 1/2"

8"

B-B SECTION

49 1/2

CHARCOAL LOADER

(PARTS TO CB-3 BARBECUE.)

1 1/8" X 11 3/8" X 23 1/2" REDWOOD DOORS (2)

INLAID CERAMIC TILE COUNTER

8" X 13 1/4" X 23 1/2" REDWOOD DOOR

18 1/2"

65 3/4"

10 3/4"

44 1/2"

24"

24"

10"

FLOOR

36 1/2"

10"

25"

25 1/2"

16 1/4"

11 3/8"

A-A

FUEL BIN

25

32"

A-A SECTION

This is rotisserie grill which goes into barbecue. Note vertical grill which holds coals behind spit.

Spit has gear at end which engages chain drive to turn. It may be moved in or out from the grill.

Under barbecue are cast iron door to the ash pit (left) and steel door opening to fuel bin (right).

Charcoal is easily scooped from fuel bin to fire above. Ash dump (left) needs occasional cleaning.

long nails embedded in the mortar, as shown in diagram.

To support the table tops, lay a row of ½-inch diameter steel reinforcing rods across the tops, embed their ends in mortar, and lay the bricks flat across them, using mortar between each brick. For a slick finished top, use four-inch square red tiles, as shown in photos.

Steel Plate in Oven

In the oven section, a row of steel rods laid across the third course of bricks serves to support a steel plate which holds the food being warmed. Under this plate is a gas burner unit which supplies the heat. Gas boosters are also provided in the barbecue pit to speed up the lighting of the charcoals.

The barbecue section should be lined with firebrick laid on edge rather than flat. Build the side walls first, then the back wall, curving it gradually inward toward the top or throat, as shown. Pack mortar behind the curved wall as you go along and be sure to allow for the rotor barbecue mechanism in masonry as you build the walls, etc.

In the throat of the barbecue, install a damper unit, as shown in diagram. Make

The warming oven has a steel plate shelf at door level set on rods. Beneath rods is gas burner.

Redwood cupboards, sink with tiled top and back splash rival the equipment of indoor kitchens.

A redwood door opens to area beneath sink which may be used for storage of cleaning materials.

Double doors of redwood open to shelves under the counter which provide additional storage space.

smoke shelf behind throat by shaping mortar into convex curve. This acts as a barrier to prevent smoke from being forced down into the barbecue by the cool air entering the chimney. Complete chimney, allowing for a 8½x17-inch flue.

Building Sink Section

The sink section is built at right angles to the main barbecue and extends 10 inches in along its left side. If desired, you can extend it all the way in (44½ inches) to bring it flush with the back side of the barbecue.

The table top is made in the same manner as the oven table top with the exception that a rectangular hole is provided in the middle to receive an 18x24-inch steel or cast iron kitchen sink.

The sink faucets can be either the type that comes as a unit mounted together with the sink, or it can be a separate mixing faucet mounted against the backsplash on the back wall, as shown in photos.

Finally, after you've finished all the masonry work, allow it to cure for at least two weeks, sprinkling it with water every day for the first week.

If you build this barbecue, you'll have one of the very finest in the country. •

OUTRIGGER BARBECUE

Slumpstone, flagstone and red brick give this unit a rustic appearance

By Louis Hochman

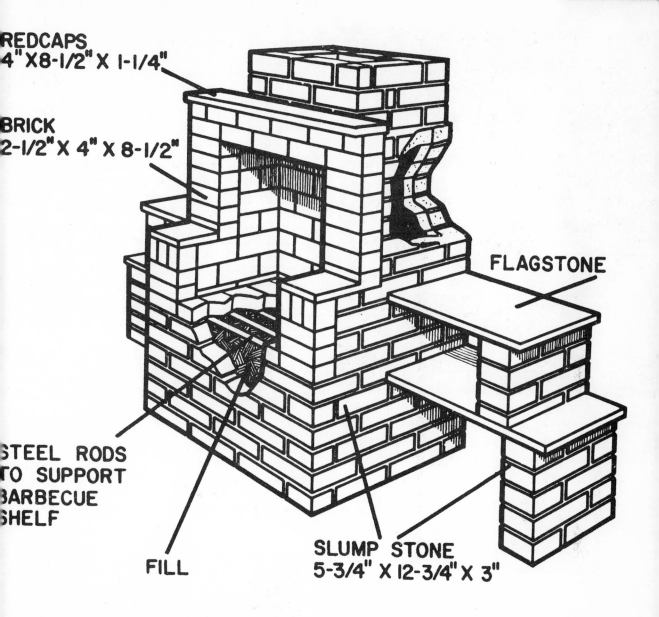

REDCAPS
4"X8-1/2"X I-1/4"

BRICK
2-1/2"X 4"X 8-1/2"

FLAGSTONE

STEEL RODS
TO SUPPORT
BARBECUE
SHELF

FILL

SLUMP STONE
5-3/4"X 12-3/4"X 3"

FOR simplicity of construction and beauty of design, the outrigger barbecue made by Outdoor Sales and Construction Co., of Sherman Oaks, California, is a sure bet.

Through the use of attractive slumpstone, flagstone and red brick, it achieves a rustic quality that sets it apart from the average commercial type barbecue, and makes it ideal for informal garden settings.

Basically, the Outrigger consists of a single unit which accommodates a 28½-inch M22 charcoal grill manufactured by The Majestic Co., Huntington, Ind. 46750. Jutting out from the sides of this main barbecue unit, are a series of flagstone table shelves which provide plenty of working space while cooking and can hold decorated potted plants, pottery, or ceramics when not in use.

The barbecue is mainly built of 5¾x12¾x3-inch slumpstone, a variety of concrete block that has a rough-hewn texture somewhat like field stone. The base is built six courses high and should measure 45 inches across the front by 2 feet 8 inches along the side. Across the top of the sixth course, lay a series of steel reinforcing rods to support the bricks of the firebox floor. The rods should be ½ inch round by 3 feet 9 inches long.

Next, lay a course of bricks across the front of the unit, then build the sides and back up with four additional slumpstone courses. The brick floor of the firebox section should then be laid across the steel

rods. Line the inside walls with brick, too, as you build up the slumpstone course. After the tenth course of slumpstone, the sides of the barbecue narrow down abruptly from the base dimension of two feet by 8 inches to a continuing width of 32½ inches. This leaves two small 8½x8¼-inch ledges on each side of the barbecue opening which are then topped off with red caps.

Face With Brick

From the sixth course up, the front of the barbecue is faced with brick, as shown. The pit opening should be 29⅜ inches wide to accommodate the Majestic grill unit. Its depth should be 19¼ inches and is lined on the inside with bricks up the back as shown in diagram. Use a 3x3-inch, 30-inch long angle iron or lintel across the top of the opening to support the top rows of bricks. Trim the top of the bricks along the front of the chimney with a row of 4x8½x1¼-inch red caps.

Slumpstone is used for the chimney and a pair of steel rods should be bridged across the top to support the front row of slumpstones. Support for the sides of the

WING TABLES are cut from inch-thick flagstone, the top table measuring 18x24, the lower 18x32 inches.

THIS VIEW of outrigger barbecue shows completed barbecue without the fireplace unit set in its place.

COMPLETED BARBECUE looks like this, uses grill made by The Majestic Co., Huntington, Indiana.

chimney is provided by tapering the brick lining on the inside wall inward at the top.

The wing tables are cut from inch-thick flagstone, the top tables measuring 18x24 inches and the lower ones, 18x32 inches. Steel pegs to support the tables where they contact the barbecue should project from the masonry between the fifth and sixth courses and the ninth and tenth courses on each side of the unit. These should be inserted when those courses are laid. The outer extremities of the tables are supported on legs of slumpstone as shown, stacking the stones five high under the lower table and four high between the lower and upper table. Allow two inches overhang past the slumpstone supports, and mortar the joints where the flagstone tables butt up against the barbecue unit proper.

The barbecue should be set on a six-inch thick concrete foundation and if this foundation does not extend to the table supports, provide concrete footings for the slumpstone legs by digging six-inch deep, 6x12-inch trenches under each support and filling these with concrete. •

RUSTIC QUALITY of barbecue sets it apart from average commercial type, makes it ideal for garden.

DIAGRAMS BELOW give all the necessary measurements needed to build the outrigger barbecue. Study them carefully, consult them from time to time. Result will be a barbecue of which you can be proud.

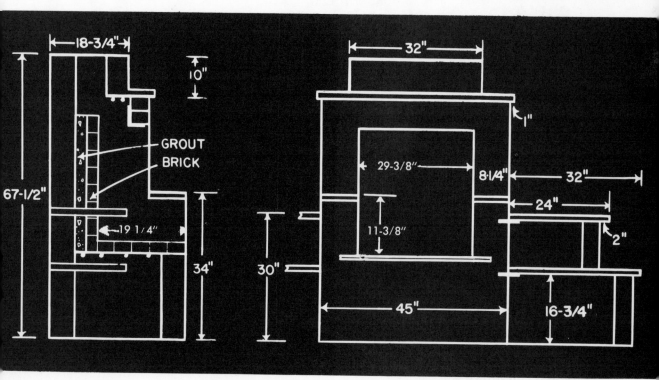

HAPPY HOLIDAY BARBECUE

This unit serves as a backyard divider as well as a barbecue

By Louis Hochman

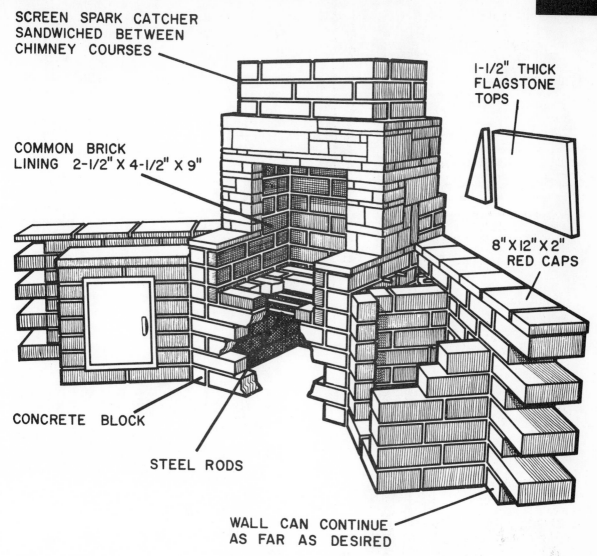

SCREEN SPARK CATCHER
SANDWICHED BETWEEN
CHIMNEY COURSES

1-1/2" THICK
FLAGSTONE
TOPS

COMMON BRICK
LINING 2-1/2" X 4-1/2" X 9"

8" X 12" X 2"
RED CAPS

CONCRETE BLOCK

STEEL RODS

WALL CAN CONTINUE
AS FAR AS DESIRED

HERE is a colorful barbecue that combines stained concrete blocks with rustic flagstone and firebrick to make outdoor picnicking a holiday event. The unit, built by California Patios of Sherman Oaks, Cal., sets diagonally into a corner of the patio and is an integral part of the concrete block wall that backs it. In fact, the wall forms the back of the barbecue and can end with the barbecue itself, or continue on for any desired distance to divide the patio or yard from the neighboring grounds.

In order to get the decorative staggered pattern in the concrete block construction, blocks of three varying lengths (6, 8, and 12 inches respectively) are used. These are stained in various colors with Kemiko concrete stain to produce the desired varicolored effect. In laying the courses, select the variety of lengths for each course that will work out to the even length required. Make this selection before mortaring any

of the blocks in place, then line them up to form the most pleasing pattern for staggered sizes and color, and mortar them into place in that order. Each following course should be selected to contrast with the previous course.

The main section of the barbecue is designed to take a 28½-inch wide M22 grill manufactured by The Majestic Company, Huntington, Indiana 46750. This unit fits snugly into the 29⅜-inch wide chamber. The base of the main section is made of concrete block eight courses high on the sides, and five courses high in the front. Across the tops of the fifth course, lay a series of parallel ⅜-inch round, 40-inch long steel reinforcing rods to support the bed of firebrick to be laid over them. Space the rods approximately three inches apart. The cavity under this firebox can be filled with dirt if desired.

Add three more courses up the sides and back above the steel rods, then set the fire

FIREPLACE UNIT in barbecue is made by The Majestic Company, Huntington, Indiana. It fits into 29⅜-inch cooking chamber.

bricks on the rods, using plenty of mortar to bond them to the rods and each other. Pave this firebox floor with firebricks to a depth of 19¼ inches; then set the rear courses vertically to form the back wall of the firebox. The inside side walls should also be lined with firebrick as shown in diagrams. If the rear wall of the barbecue unit is never seen, it can be built with concrete block. Otherwise, flagstone rock should be used above the eighth course of concrete block. From the eighth course on, the sides and front of the barbecue unit are built with flagstone rock, selecting sizes and strips to form the most pleasing design and texture. The two ledges that flank the grill unit are topped with 8½x12-inch rectangles of inch-thick flagstone.

The flagstone portion of the walls should extend to a height of 5 feet 1½ inches from

MATERIALS NEEDED:

500 lbs. flagstone rock

65 fire bricks (8½x4x2½)

25 concrete blocks (6x4x12)

25 concrete blocks (6x4x8)

4 concrete blocks (6x4x6)

10 red caps (2x8x12)

170 concrete blocks (6x4x16)

15 concrete blocks (6x4x14)

2 Flagstone tops, 20x30x1-inch thick

1 Flagstone top, 18x20-inch cut in half diagonally

2 Flagstone tops, 8½x12-inch

2 Steel reinforcing rods, ⅜-inch round by 42-inch long

5 Steel reinforcing rods, ⅜-inch round by 40-inch long

1 3x3 angle iron, 40-inch long

1 Spark arrestor 12x36-inch, ½-inch mesh 12 gauge

2 14x20-inch Burr Steel Doors

1 28-inch wide Albert Control-A-Fire Grill unit

1 Hood 30-inch wide at top flanging out to 38-inch

1 ton plaster sand

½ ton pea gravel (For foundation mix)

3 sacks plastic cement

For the mortar, mix 5 parts sand to 1 part cement.

For the Foundation, mix 3 parts sand to 4 parts gravel and 1 part cement.

the ground, at which point the chimney section begins. For this section, we go back to concrete block, building it three courses high and sandwiching a 20x36-inch rectangle of 12-gauge, ½-inch wire mesh between the second and third course, as shown in diagram. This wire mesh serves as the spark catcher. Because the chimney has narrower dimensions than the main unit, two steel rods, ⅜ inch round by 42 inches long, must be bridged across the top opening to form a support for the front row of blocks used in the chimney.

Extending at an angle of 45 degrees on each side of this main unit are two storage compartments topped with flagstone tabletops which provide generous work surfaces. Start by laying out the back walls of unstained concrete block, setting these walls at 45-degree angles to the sides of the bar-

becue unit. These walls form the backs of the storage compartments and should be eight courses high, topped with 8x12x2-inch red caps. The storage units are then built up against this back wall, making them 28 inches wide at the front and seven courses high. Because of the difficulty of cutting the flagstone top in one piece, it is better to do it in two pieces, one piece measuring 20x30 inches and the other a triangle measuring 18x20 inches on its right angle sides. A simple way is to take an 18x20 inch rectangle of flagstone and cut it diagonally in half to make the two triangles needed on each side of the barbecue.

In the front of the storage units, leave 14x20 inch masonry openings as shown to accommodate 14x20 inch Burr steel doors.

The concrete foundation for the main unit should be at least six inches thick. •

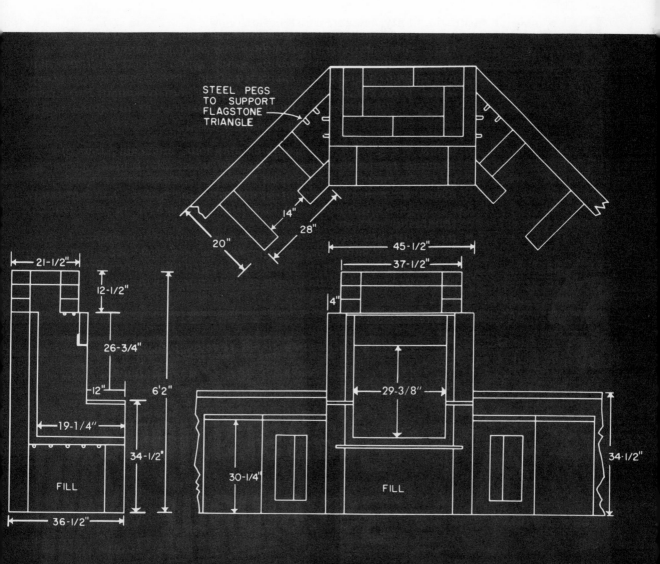

For an ultra-modern touch,
Louis Hochman recommends a

FLAGSTONE TABLE

FOR a table of rustic simplicity, rugged construction, and modern design, you can't beat a flagstone table as designed and built by Carl Pugh of the Ace Brick and Patio Supply Corporation in Van Nuys, California.

The colorful, shale-type stone used in these tables is available in one form or another in all parts of the country and can be cut into any desired shape—free form, round, oval, rectangular, square, etc.,—and set on a variety of wooden or wrought iron legs to produce an attractive table suitable for patio or living room use.

Aside from the natural beauty of this material, a flagstone table is one of the most durable pieces of furniture you can build. It will resist sun, weather and water. When properly sealed and waxed, it will also be grease-resistant.

The stone comes in various color hues, depending upon what part of the country it comes from. Arizona flagstone comes in pinks, reds, yellows, tans and buffs. Utah stones run blues to greens; Colorado, reds to pinks; and Tennessee, blues to grays. Tennessee also produces a colorful blue-gray slate which is ideal for table tops, but unfortunately, cannot be cut by hand. However, for a nominal charge, your local stone dealer can cut it perfectly to any desired shape with his diamond bandsaw, which produces a smooth, finished square edge.

In selecting the stone for your table top, pick one that is at least three inches larger on all sides than you need. It is necessary to have at least this much margin to get a good cut when chiseling out your piece. Pick a stone that is evenly thick throughout, not less than ¾ inch thick. Carl Pugh's stones average about one inch thick, with some running as thick as 1½ inches.

The stone should also be free of any internal cracks or fractures. Any small crack leading in from the edge of the stone will—as with glass—tend to continue on through the stone when you try to cut it. Another thing to watch out for is that the stone has no obvious laminations which would indicate that it is actually two layers of stone rather than one. Laminations can be seen by studying the edge of the stone. If a lamination line runs all around the stone, don't use it. Short vague lamination lines, however, do not neces-

Weather-proof free form flagstone table
is ideal for outdoor dining location.

Flagstone top is supported by the welded structural steel rod frame and legs.

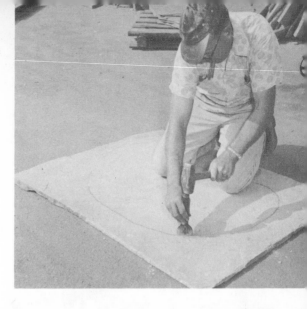

First mark off free form outline on flagstone.

Score the outline with hammer and chisel as shown.

Go over line a second time with hammer and chisel.

On the second time around, stone breaks off neatly.

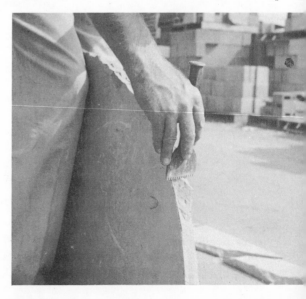

Rough edges are nipped off with a pair of pincers.

Larger knobs are shaved with hammer and chisel.

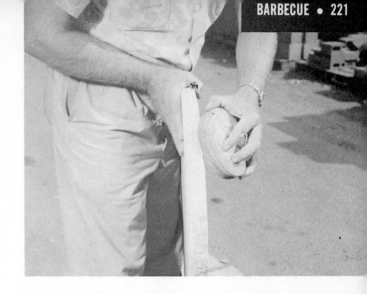

sarily impair a stone's quality for table use.

To cut flagstone, mark your outline on it with chalk. Then with a three-inch stone chisel and a four-pound stone mason's hammer, score a line in the stone following the chalked outline. Usually, on the second pass, the stone will crack neatly through under the scored line. Jagged edges can then be either pinched off with a large pair of pincers, or cut away with the chisel, as shown in photos. A carborundum block can then be used to rub off the sharp flakes of stone and smooth the edges to a finished look. For further finishing, use emery cloth to remove blemishes and chisel marks.

To get a smooth, perfectly straight line cut, you can use a Skilsaw fitted with a carborundum blade. Set the blade to a cutting depth of about ⅛ inch and use the power saw to score a shallow groove in the stone along the line it is to be cut on. Then break the stone on this line by using the hammer and chisel along the grooved track. Another method of cutting a straight line without a power saw is to set the stone on a length of angle iron which is laid on the ground with its "V" shape pointing upward. The peak of the V should rest directly under the line to be scored. Next, with hammer and chisel, score the line along edge of angle iron. On the second pass, the stone will break neatly on the line.

Legs for Table

Legs for your table can be made in several ways. You can form your own by bending structural steel rods and welding them to a steel rod frame, or you can use any type of commercially available wrought iron or wooden leg set. If you can't do your own welding, any blacksmith or automobile repair shop will do the welding for you for a reasonable fee. Attractive legs can also be made from short lengths of ½-inch pipe painted black. Use plastic or rubber crutch tips on their ends.

The store-bought variety of wrought iron and wooden legs can be attached to a base platform of ¾-inch plywood on which the stone top can be set. When designing the platform frame, make it rectangular in shape so that the legs will be easier to corner evenly, and make it as large as possible without letting it jut out past the edge of the stone top. This will give the stone a maximum of support. The stone is then laid on the frame and its weight will keep it in place. For rectangular tables, make the frames of heavy angle iron and set the stone top right into the angle iron frame.

To make the stone grease-proof, first flush it down with water to remove all

Finish smoothing process with an old grindstone.

Place top on pipe legs welded to a hot air grate.

Free form flagstone table is now ready for use.

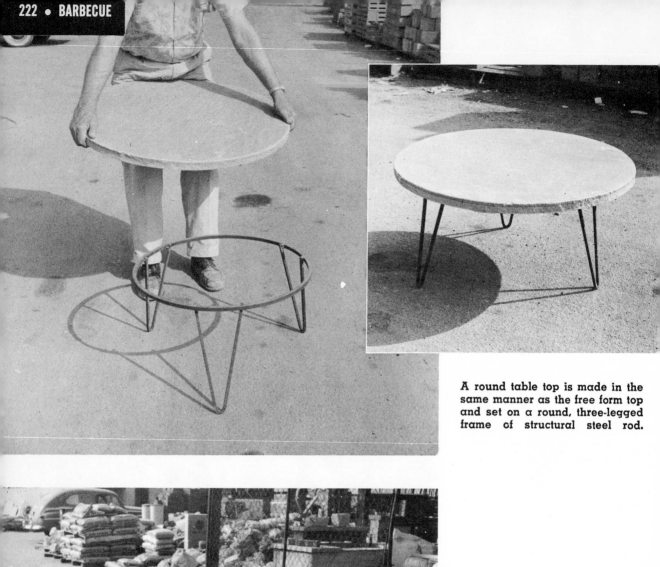

A round table top is made in the same manner as the free form top and set on a round, three-legged frame of structural steel rod.

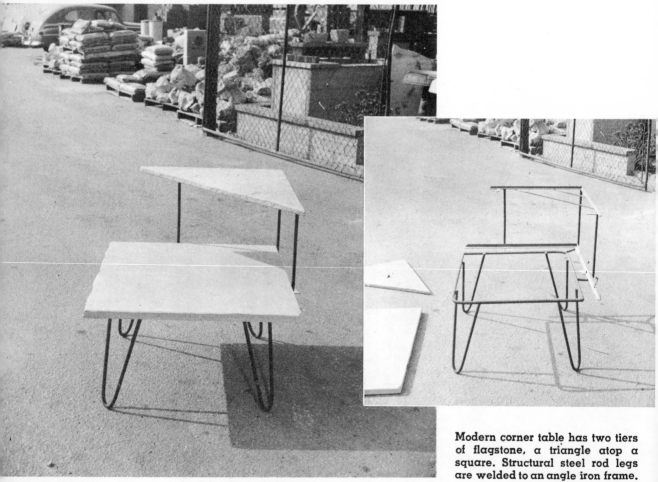

Modern corner table has two tiers of flagstone, a triangle atop a square. Structural steel rod legs are welded to an angle iron frame.

stone dust and foreign particles. If these are not removed, they will streak badly when the sealer is applied. After the stone has been washed and dried, apply a sealer (Transcel No. 5 made by Rohloff and Company of Hollywood, California, is fine) which is available at most building stone dealers. When this sealer has dried, wax the stone surface with a good paste wax. Treewax, also available at stone dealers, is ideal for this. Besides rendering the stone grease-proof and giving its surface a polished sheen, the sealer coat has the added quality of bringing out and enhancing the natural colors of the stone.

Flagstone tables can be made to stand 18 to 20 inches high and serve as coffee tables, or 29 inches high to serve as regular dining tables. Dining tables, however, should be oval or rectangular in shape, the rectangular ones providing more seating area and thus being more practical. •

Ready-made wrought iron legs are screwed to a ¾-inch plywood rectangle to support a graceful oval table top cut to shape from flagstone slab.

Basement Preparations

You *can* convert that dark, dank basement into attractive living space. Start here

A BASEMENT comes with its own built-in problems. The area is below ground for the most part. It's in contact with the earth on almost all sides and the windows, of necessity, are small. All of which cuts down on light and encourages enough dampness to grow fungus on your shirt.

Before cutting loose on the decorative aspects of basement remodeling, do a thorough job of moisture-proofing so you will really be comfortable in the finished area. For the most part, you'll have to match the treatment to the seriousness of the problem. Ticked off below are the various problems and some suggested remedies.

Hydrostatic Pressure

This impressive engineering term refers to the force of the water in the earth that's pushing against your basement walls from the outside. Seriousness varies. In some cases, pressure can create slight dampness in the outside walls. When raised to grand-slam proportions, hydrostatic pressure can actually cause little geysers of water to spurt out of crevices in the wall. Great on picture postcards from Italy, but not so nifty in the basement.

The sure-fire, never-fail cure is a rough, involved, laborious process. If your basement is cursed with this problem you may have to go through with the complete fix-it process. If the trouble is limited to a slight amount of dampness, odds are quite good that

Exterior waterproofing is a job, but worth it if necessary. Lay drain line around the foundation.

Fiber pipe such as Bermico is easy to handle. A large range of fittings (Ts, Els, etc.) are sold.

Who would have believed it? This modern recreation room was constructed in an "ordinary" basement.

Fiber pipe ends have preformed, interlocking fittings. Cushion with block and hammer together.

Fiber pipe can be cut to length with handsaw. Perforated type (has holes in the bottom) is used.

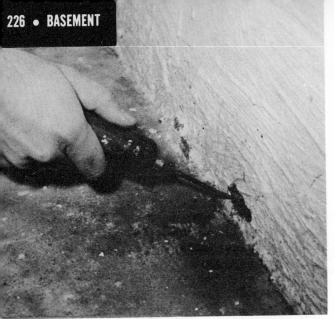

Inside basement use ice pick to probe for leaks. Pay special attention to wall and floor joint.

Wet walls can result from water trapped in hollow block walls. Drill release hole near the floor.

you can make the area pleasantly dry with an inside treatment. Also, if the walls seem dry but water comes in through a few chinks in the wall or floor, an interior patch job may still do the trick. At any rate it's worth a try before starting on an involved exterior preventive. On the other hand, if the walls are really in bad shape, if the moisture comes out like a fountain, the hand of fate has slated you for the whole deal. Let's start with the large scale treatment.

Exterior Waterproofing

As the first step in exterior waterproofing, start digging. Dig a trench all the way around the foundation wall of the basement right down to the footings. Scrap away the

Pitch a run of drain pipe down into a dry well about 10 ft. from house. Also run in downspout.

earth from the masonry wall and brush it clean. You can see why we hesitated in presenting this step.

Build up a protective membrane to hold the water at bay. The time tested method is to first coat the masonry with black roofing cement and press a strip of saturated asphalt paper in place. You'll probably have to use several horizontal rows of paper. Overlap the seams by 6-8 in. and be sure to apply more cement at the joint. Once the whole wall is covered, brush on more cement and start another layer right on top. It's a good idea to stagger the joints. In this manner, build up a membrane of three or even four layers of tar paper all the way around the entire wall.

Before you kick the dirt back into the trench you've dug, it's a good idea to include some drainage tile. This, too, should be in the form of a ring circling the basement foundation. First dump about 6 in. of coarse crushed rock into the bottom of the trench. Then position the drainage tile on top. You can use one of two types.

The old stand-by is to make the drain line of agricultural tile. This is an unglazed tile that comes in short (1-ft.) lengths. Line the sections up on top of the crushed rock and leave about ¼-in. gap between them. Tear small strips of tar paper and cover the joints. Don't wrap the strips around the joint. The trick is to cover the top and sides only so that water will be able to enter the pipe through the bottom slot.

Dig a connecting trench to lead the water off. This, too, should get the crushed rock plus tile treatment. Hook into the run of drain around the foundation. After all the pipes are in place, dump enough crushed

Next step is to dry area thoroughly before plugging. Best for this job is a hydraulic cement.

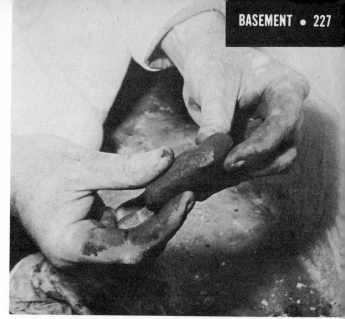

Form plug by mixing powder with water to make stiff putty. When it gets warm, it's ready for use.

rock on top to cover them (3-4 in.), add a long strip of tar paper on top and kick the dirt back in.

Lighter, quicker to install and handier to heft is a material called bituminized fiber pipe. But don't ask for it by this handle at the local building supply company because they might toss you into the street. More familiarly, the pipe is known as Orangeburg or Bermico. By either name, it's a lightweight, almost indestructible material that comes in long sections (up to 8 ft. and in several diameters). The ends have a preformed interlocking fitting that goes together neatly with a slight clong of a hammer. Also available are a whole range of fittings (T's, El's, etc.). You can slice this pipe to proper length with a regular saw; no pipe cutters, no threaders necessary.

Installation procedure is pretty much the same as for agricultural tile except that you should use the perforated version for the run around the perimeter of the house. This is the same material except that one or two rows of holes are already drilled. Just make sure you position it so that the holes are facing downward. For the run from the house foundation to the dry well use the same diameter pipe without holes.

So what do you do with the water once you have it neatly slucking through the pipes? You dig a dry well to get rid of it. There's one consolation here. If you don't break your back on this phase of the project, odds are well in your favor that you'll have the physical moxie to finish off the rest of the remodeling.

Building a Dry Well

Locate the dry well about 10 ft. away from the house. If your land is on a slope, you're in luck because it's necessary to maintain a pitch to the pipe that feeds into the dry well. All of which means that the top of the dry well is slightly below the level of the drain. Bottom of the dry well? It's down from there.

Just like the name says, a dry well is a big hole that you dig in the ground, but you're not looking for water, just trying to get rid of it. You'll need a hole about 5 ft. in diameter and about the same depth. Please note that the depth is measured from the level of the drain pipe down. You may have to do some digging before you can even start measuring.

Line the pit with cesspool block. This is a rough cinder block that has holes in it. Lay the blocks dry without mortar and leave the joints slightly open. Toss about 4 in. of coarse crushed rock in the bottom of the finished well. Lead in the length of drain pipe. Cover over the pit with a standard cesspool lid. This is a hefty, cast concrete affair. Fill in the spaces between the outside of the blocks and the hole that you've dug with more crushed rock. Finally, cover over the whole rig with earth.

One other drainage problem: It's a good idea to lead the runoff water from the gutters away from the house. Since you have gone to all the trouble of digging a dry well, you might just as well feed this surplus liquid into it and know that you've achieved a complete cure.

If the drain spout has an elbow at the end, slice this off with a hack saw. Attach a right angle fitting onto a length of solid Bermico. Add another length (a short one) into the other leg of the angle and attach a fitting called a join elbow on the end of this. Fit the end of the downspout into the join elbow and shore up the base of the elbow to hold it in position. Run whatever lengths of Bermico you need to reach over to the dry well, clobbering each by tapping on a wood block held against the end of the pipe. *Never* hammer directly on the pipe. Always protect the pipe or fitting with a wood block or else you may chew up the end and never be able to attach the next length.

Seal the joint between the join elbow and the downspout by forcing oakum into the crevice. You can buy it at most hardware and all plumbing supply stores. Finally apply a layer of cement over the oakum and slope it down neatly so it sheds water.

Interior Waterproofing

If you were born under a lucky configuration of the heavens, you may be able to get by with a simple interior waterproofing job. Although there are quite a few products on the market designed for this purpose, the most effective incorporate the new epoxy compounds. One trade-named product along this line is Epoxite (Community Waterproofing Co., 10 Redcoat Rd., Westport, Conn.). Although several firms put out such an item, this company will sell in small quantities. Since they put up the stuff in 1 lb. cans, you can order only what you need.

Let's get a few facts straight. This is not a paint that you slobber all over the cellar walls. Not at five bucks a pound you don't. However, since most water seepage comes in through cracks in the wall (especially at the point where the wall meets the floor) or through the floor itself, you can seal off the basement by treating only the problem areas.

Figure out how much material you need. One lb. will cover about 25 sq. ft. of dense masonry surface. Porous surfaces such as cinder block sop up the stuff and more is required. Also, since cinder block walls themselves may admit water (not just through cracks), you may be involved in a far more extensive treatment.

Assuming that spot waterproofing will do the trick, find out where the water is entering. This is easy. Just mop up the watery mess and then watch where it flows through the wall. Use an ice pick to probe for leaks, scraping away crumbling cement or mortar. Pay special attention to the joint between wall and floor.

If the base of the walls seem wet but you can't find any direct leak, water may have collected in the hollow interior of the wall

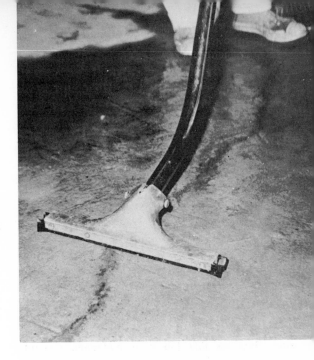

Before applying epoxy to walls and floor, dry basement thoroughly and vacuum up all dust and dirt.

(if it's made of cement or cinder block). In this case, use a masonry drill to bore through the wall close to the floor and allow the water to escape.

Clean out all the deep cracks and holes and plug them before applying the epoxy. For this job use hydraulic cement. (Quick Plug or Waterplug are two brands and there are others on the market.) Most come as a powder that you mix with water to form a stiff putty. Roll the stuff into small cone shaped globs in your hands. After a bit you'll notice that the material is beginning to get warm. This is your cue to ram the plug into the hole and pack it in as firmly as you can. Work like a maniac at this stage because the cement sets very rapidly. It will expand in place and seal off the opening.

Using Epoxy on Walls

Dry out the basement thoroughly. Bring electric heaters down there, use a torch, open the windows (in warm weather), use a fan . . . anything to get the surfaces dry. Although the epoxy will act as a highly efficient barrier to water, it won't stick to a wet surface. If necessary, you may have to split up the job into several stages. Dry out one section and waterproof it. Then move on to the next area until you have worked your way around the room.

The epoxy is packaged in two parts to separate the resin from the chemical that activates it. Mix them together (use the entire contents of each can) and then stir like a mad dog for at least two minutes. To apply the stuff, don't use a good brush. It's

Be sure to brush a thick coating of epoxy on wall-floor joint. Use a cheap, throw-away brush.

Universal treatment is to asphalt damp-proof wall after using epoxy first to seal off wall.

almost impossible to clean. Instead buy a miserable, cheap, unhappy brush and toss it away when the job is finished.

Be sure you have cleaned up all the assorted bits of crumbled mortar, wire-brushed away the whitewash and swept up the area generally before starting. Epoxy will bond to dry, clean stone or to paint that is holding firmly to the surface.

Brush a coating onto the wall-floor joint. Don't get stingy or try to do a cabinet-maker's job. Just slap the material on in a thick, messy coating. Extend the stripe 3 in. up the wall and about 9 in. out onto the floor. Those hairline cracks on wall and floor should be bridged with a heavy 4 in.-wide stripe.

Temperature is important. It's impossible to handle the epoxy if the mercury dips below 45 degrees. If you can nudge the thermostat up to 70 degrees the material will dry overnight. Do not become discouraged if it takes two or even three coats to completely stop the leaks. Just slob one on top of another after the necessary drying period.

Don't worry too much about the decorative value of the new coating. It has none (dries to a dark amber hue). Once you have the water neatly fenced out, you can paint over the stuff with a rubber base paint in any tint you like.

Do any other messy preparation jobs while the room is still bare. If the floor is coated with an accumulation of wax and ground-in dirt, clean off the whole works. Use standard wax remover (paint store item) mixed according to the directions on

the package. Swab the mixture over the surface and mop it up.

How to Remove Paint

Removing paint is a little rougher. Actually there are two ways the job can be handled, but neither one is fully delightful. Most standard paint removers will do the trick. Fumes are quite unpleasant and even dangerous. If you select this method, use all safety precautions. Provide plenty of ventilation (using fans to force the movement of air if necessary), cover up well to protect your skin and wear goggles so none of the remover can splatter in your eyes. Following the instructions on the label, apply the remover, allow sufficient time for it to work and then mop up the paint. The easiest system is to use a rubber squeegee on a long handle.

You may prefer to apply a wash-away remover so that the chemical and softened paint can be hosed down the drain. One word of caution: Some removers leave a waxy film behind. If the instructions suggest that you mop the clean floor with denatured alcohol after it is free of paint, be sure to do it. Otherwise, the film of wax will prevent any finish from sticking to the surface.

The other system requires a floor sanding machine. Hook a belt of very rough paper onto the drum and start grinding away. The noise will be horrendous and the dust billowy, but the method does avoid the need for widespread application of chemicals. Here again there are safety precautions. Wear a mask over your nose and

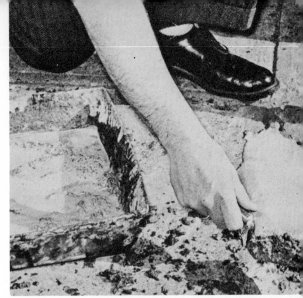

Photos courtesy U. S. Rubber Co.

Rubberized concrete, good for holes and cracks in floors, is liquid rubber mixed with concrete.

Simply trowel in rubberized mixture and smooth. It sticks well to the old concrete and is durable.

Expanding plugs are used for building on masonry. Right is lead anchor and screw, left, fiber.

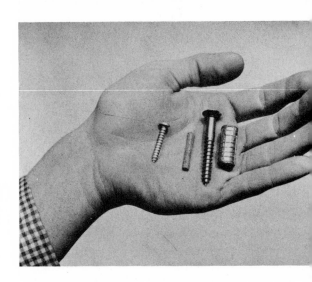

mouth so that you don't breathe in the fine dust.

There are a couple of other common problems involving basement floors. Quite frequently the cement surface will be perfectly sound but the top layer continually turns to powder and comes off in a fine dust. You can sweep the surface from now to next St. Swithen's day and never get all the dust up. The best solution is a surface hardener. You'll find this sold at most building supply companies and lumberyards (Dus-Top is one brand and some other firms make similar products). Following the instructions on the label, swab it onto the concrete. It will harden it so you can successfully paint the floor or put down tile.

How about holes and cracks in the floor? These repairs aren't hard. Your best bet here is a rubberized concrete. Use a preparation such as U.S. Rubber's Laticrete (again there are other brands). Mix the liquid rubber with a dry packaged concrete mix instead of using water. The end result is a concrete mortar that will stick like crazy to the old concrete, even in a thin layer. It also has good water and weather resistance. After you have chipped out the loose or crumbling cement, trowel in the rubberized mixture and smooth it off just as you would the standard material.

Building on Concrete

Basements present one additional hurdle, but like the rest, this is not too difficult to vault. Fastening anything up to the con-

crete walls or floors is not like pounding a nail into nice gentle wood. In general there are four main ways to fasten into cement; plugs of various types, cement nails, adhesive anchors and stud gun. Let's takes these one at a time.

Any kind of expanding *plug* must fit into a carefully drilled hole in the masonry. If you have the strength and determination of a mad dog, you can do this with a star drill and a hammer. Hold the drill in position and whong it with the hammer. Give the drill a slight turn and hit it again. Keep up this process until you have pounded the proper depth hole. Diameter of the hole depends on the size of the star drill and you'll find this information detailed on the shank.

Now. For the good folks with sense, invest a buck or so in a good quality carbide tip bit for use with an electric drill. These are tipped with a very hard material that

Easiest way to seat a large number of anchors for furring strips is to use electric drill and a good quality carbide-tip bit.

After anchors are seated, furring strips are installed by driving the long screws through predrilled holes into the anchors.

actually bites through the rugged cement. There are a couple of precautions, however. If you allow the bit to turn too swiftly, you are quite likely to burn it out or at least dull the edges. If you have a ½-in. electric drill, use it. You don't need the extra power, it's just that drills of this size are geared down and the chuck turns more slowly. A speed reducer on a regular ¼-in. drill will do splendidly. Failing either of these, use your regular drill and hope for the best.

Expanding fasteners or plugs come in several types. Most common and quite reliable is a lead anchor. But then, you will find the shelves at your local hardware loaded with plugs of plastic, fiber, etc. They all work in the same manner.

Drill a hole through the wood member that's to be fastened in place. Hold the wood against the wall where it will be attached and mark the spot where the hole meets the wall. Then drill a hole in the masonry right there. Although this word of caution is hardly necessary, the size of the hole must match the size of the plug and this data is detailed on the package.

Push a plug into the hole. You will probably have to give it a slight tap to seat it properly. Slip a long screw through the hole in the wood and turn it into the plug. The plug will expand in the hole as the screw is driven home and lock itself securely in place. One more point: Each size plug takes a certain screw size and some times these are special bits of hardware, so buy the whole kit together.

There are other variations on this theme. Some plugs are semimachined affairs that must be inserted and tightened into place using a special tool. Long bolts go through the wood and tighten into the threaded inside section of the plug. You may, for some reason of your own, prefer these, but the added expense is rarely warranted. As for lead versus plastic or fiber plugs, the author has never found the selection to be a critical one.

Concrete Nails

These are fatter and tougher but they drive just like regular nails. The only problem is that you will be hammering them into concrete, not wood, and this takes a heavier hammer plus more stuff backing it up. To use concrete nails, first drill a hole through the wood. Neglect this procedure and the thick-shanked nails will split the wood. Hold the wood in position, slip a nail through the hole and hammer it into the concrete. A small short-handled sledge helps this job along and you'll have less trouble with hammer rebound.

There are drawbacks to this method. If you have quite a few strips to fasten up, you may space the nails so close together they will make the cement crumble. Then, too, if the wall is in very bad condition, this heavy-handed treatment can chip out patches. On reasonably decent cement, it's a perfectly workable method, however, and well worth a try.

Adhesive Anchors

Thanks to rubber base adhesive, you can glue up furring strips or even studs. Buy a batch of surface anchors plus some of the proper adhesive (Miracle Cement is the old stand-by, but there are others). This is a black, gummy mastic. The anchors are perforated metal plates about 2 in. square or a little larger. Welded into the center is bit of hardware (bolt, nail, prong, clamp, etc.). Just be sure you use the proper one for the job.

To hold up furring strips, use a nail anchor; pipes take a special clamp, insulation supports come with a folding clasp, etc. They are all fastened to the wall in the same way. Smear the adhesive on the back of the plate. No need to get fancy. Just glob it on from the tube in a layer about $\frac{1}{16}$-in. thick. Immediately press it to the wall with a slight twisting and sliding motion. This will squeeze some of the glue through the holes in the anchor and also bond the plate to the wall. Allow about 24 hours for the adhesive to set before applying anything to it.

Once the anchors are in place, it's a cinch to fasten up furring strips. Just impale the wood on the row of nails and drive the point through until the wood rests against the metal anchor plate. Clinch the nails for a secure bond.

Studs can be held in place by using a bolt-type anchor. Drill a hole in the wood so the bolts can slip through and draw the nuts up firmly to hold the stud in place. Insulation is simply impaled on the sheet metal projection and the notched end folded over in two directions. Other sys-

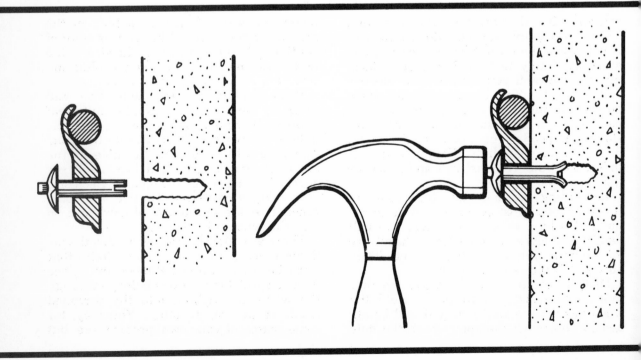

Adhesive anchors can be used, are easy to install. Coat with proper adhesive and put on wall.

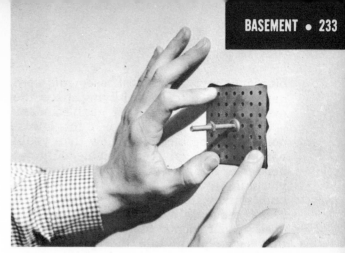

Adhesive anchors are perforated metal plates about 2 in. with bolt, prong, etc., in the center.

First step in installing furring strips is to lay out the lines for the anchors and put them in.

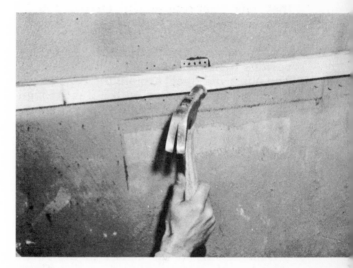

Strips go up quickly with anchors in. This type of adhesive anchor has a nail welded in center.

tems for this last job use a nail-type anchor with a special jumbo-sized sheet metal washer that slides over the nail and clamps in place. Just finger through the stock at the hardware store until you find the exact type you need.

Stud Guns

Here we have the fastest, easiest method of fastening onto the toughest masonry. Made by Remington Arms, these gadgets use a special type of blank cartridge to literally shoot a stud into the masonry. Expensive? Sure they *are* expensive. The smallest version sells for about $35, and the industrial model for well over a hundred. If you plan on doing much work of this type, the little gun is a useful investment. However, either type may be rented from many forward looking hardware stores. They will also sell you the cartridges plus whatever studs you need.

Cartridges are sized to match the type of stud and the kind of surface they will penetrate. Studs come in any nail type, a bolt threaded on either the inside or the outside, or in several other varieties. To use this tool, you don't bother drilling holes; you just shoot. The metal fastener is driven right through the wood into the masonry.

A word of caution. Although these devices have all sorts of safety precautions built into them, they can be dangerous weapons. Only fire studs into walls that you know are solid masonry. Never use the stud gun on a wood wall. The metal projectile will zip right through the wall and keep traveling. You can easily lose a rich uncle this way.

Ceiling Preparations

This is a good point to finish off the ceiling preparations. In most cases you'll probably want to drop the ceiling to cover a maze of pipes, electric cables and the like. This phase of the job usually requires a bit of juggling. Since most basements were never designed for useful living space, the overhead area is usually a jumbled mess.

Obviously, if you just pick the lowest point and drop a ceiling below that, you'll wind up with an area suitable only for bent-over midgets. On the other hand, if you shift all the various electric and water lines so they run between the joists, you'll break the family budget. If absolutely necessary, relocate the pipes and cables that severely cut into the space. Don't bother about those near the edge of the room. Concentrate on the obstructions that cut down on usability. If your basement is an average one, chances are good that this compromise will enable you to clear a sizable area right up to the underside of the joists.

Let's delve into the tricks of hiding the various items that extend below this line. The pipes and ducts around the edge of the room can be concealed with a light trough or cornice, stashed behind a fake beam or incorporated into the cabinets that you will probably build. Wires or small pipes can be tucked away behind some jumbo-sized molding. Continue the same molding all the way across the wall so that your subterfuge isn't too obvious. Although you will not put up the trim at this time, it's a good idea to install structural supports for it.

Obstructions in the center of the room can't be palmed off quite so easily. Steel beams can be covered with wood to make fake wood beams which are a little easier to live with. Maybe you can shift the position of a room divider or free-standing storage unit so that the top part can cover the duct or pipe. Your ingenuity will have to be your guide.

Basement Entries

In the sorry event that you live in a house that does not have an outside basement entrance, you can add the entry yourself. The job can be a tricky one, however. You have to punch through the foundation wall and dig out vast amounts of dirt. Each shovelful doesn't weigh very much but it takes an unbelievable number to fill a wheelbarrow. And the wheelbarrow loads that have to be removed? One shudders to tally.

So use a modicum of sense. Have a builder or architect check over the foundation before you start chipping out blocks. Unless family finances are scraping bottom, hire out the excavation work. A man seated comfortably on a back hoe can do the job in a couple of hours. If not, buy

Stud gun, triggered by hammer blow, shoots stud in masonry. Some hardware stores will rent them.

First step in building a basement entry is to excavate, then break through the basement wall.

a case of beer, make sandwiches and call up every friend you ever had.

Excavate an area about 5 ft. square to expose the foundation wall where the doorway will be placed. (Assuming the basement is an average one that's about six to nine steps below ground.) Play it safe and include a 45-degree slope around the sides to prevent a cave-in.

With a sledge hammer and a couple of mason's chisels, break through the basement wall. If you have the foresight to do this job from the inside, you can keep a firm footing instead of sloshing about in the muck outside.

Undoubtedly you will be using one of those slanting hatchway doors to close off the opening. Check through the manufacturer's literature and get the exact dimensions. That hole you dug in the ground has to be lined with masonry block to make an extension of the foundation. Exact size here depends upon the door frame size.

Entry hole is lined with cinder block to extend foundation. Exact size depends on the door size.

Waterproof outside of extension using asphalt preparation. Coat with asphalt paper if needed.

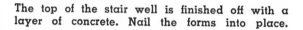

The top of the stair well is finished off with a layer of concrete. Nail the forms into place.

Completed basement entry is protected by steel cover. The unit in the photos is made by Bilko.

Build a rough wood form at the bottom of your pit and pour concrete footings. Then build up the wall, staggering the joints of the blocks for extra strength. Bond carefully where the new block meets the old house foundation. Carefully waterproof the outside of the masonry using the black, gucky foundation coating made for this purpose. If you have a severe water problem in the basement, apply a membrane of a number of layers of saturated asphalt paper and mastic as recommended earlier in this chapter. You can then shovel the dirt back against the new foundation walls.

Installing the hatchway door itself only takes about four hours. If you have a set of exterior basement steps covered by a battered old wooden cover you might start listening at this point. The procedure, after you have ripped away the old mess, is the same. The unit in the photos is made by Bilco. Although other manufacturers make these units, installation is similar.

Open up the package and assemble the frame. The gadget has to fit firmly against the side of the house, so position the frame on top of the masonry and mark where it meets the siding. Cut out the clapboard or shingles. You don't have to worry with this step if you have a masonry house. Attach the doors to the frame and joggle it slightly to make sure it's square and that the doors line up properly.

Very carefully, so you don't shift position of the frame, remove the doors. You'll notice a few holes in the bottom of the frame. Mark the position of these on the masonry underneath. Slide away the frame and drill holes in the masonry to take expanding plugs. Seat the lead plugs, replace the frame and tighten it down. Put back the doors and install any miscellaneous hardware. Finally, calk the framework to make it weather-tight and replace any needed house siding. Steps? The more ingenious shop man can take care of that. •

Building a Basement Guest Room

It's hide-away and won't interfere yet beautifully designed for comfort

IF you like sheer magic this concealed bedroom for two, which needs only 2 ft. of depth in your room can be yours with very little effort.

It not only houses two beds in a wall area of little over 8 ft. of width, but it also stores all the bedding, including extra winter blankets, holds books for the guests, a portable radio, and has enough cabinet space to store the belongings of long-staying guests.

A night table which serves both beds disappears into the wall when not in use.

The upholstered headboards open up and form a reclining support for reading

Left, finished unit fully opened has twin beds, two linen cabinets with sliding doors, plenty of drawer space, reclining device for reading and TV and extra space for convenience.

Top right, all the walls and ceiling were furred out and, as with all of the basement exterior walls, covered with polyethylene sheets to help insulate against moisture. Center closet was removed later.

Lower right, shows the center cabinet area open for inspection. Note the third drawer is refashioned with a Formica topping to form a handy side table unit for in-bed snackers.

in bed, with built-in illumination in the ceiling providing the light for it.

The indirect lighting on the top of this built-in unit provides for the beautiful special effect which will give you great pride in telling your guests that this is where they are going to spend the night.

After the wall is furred out with 2x3's and the electric installation is completed, cover the studs with polyethylene sheeting for insulation. The walls are paneled next, with ¼-in. prefinished Nakora V-Plank paneling. This wall now will serve for a back for the entire unit and all cabinets are made without back, mounted to the wall with 3-in.-wide back support strips.

From now on the construction is simple. The center storage part is a complete unit as shown in diagram. It has prefabricated plastic drawers which come with ready made steel frames. The two outside units which house the beds are actually mounted in part to the center unit.

Due to the fact that the walls were paneled in the back and sides of this room it was only necessary to build the base where the beds sit on it and to mount a ceiling that unites all three units. In other words, the ceiling is mounted against cleats all around.

Finally, a 3-in.-wide front strip mounted to the edge of the ceiling, ties the whole

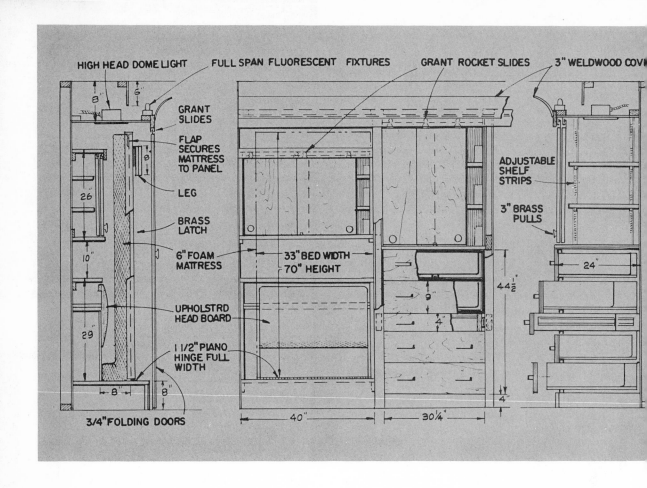

The entire unit is only 24″ deep with doors closed. Light above is fluorescent and indirect.

For privacy there are folding doors which enclose the entire unit. This allows full use of room.

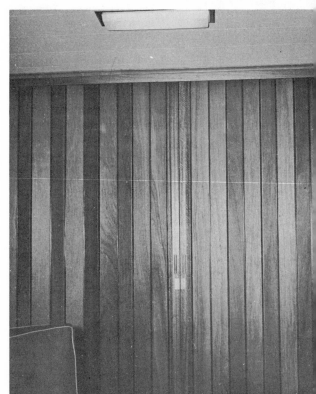

thing together and provides for a mounting base of the folding door hardware for both built-in beds. The inside of the bed units is simple. The top cabinet consists of a top, a bottom and two sides, with two back support strips. The shelves are adjustable and the two sliding doors are hung with Grant Rocket slides.

The bottom cabinet, the headboard cabinet, is made in the same way as the top cabinet except that it has a top shelf, which is mounted permanently and which acts as a support base for the headboard's reclining bracket. At the same time, the shelf can be used for storage of books, etc.

The headboard is ½-in.-thick plywood with a 1x2-in. frame around it, mounted on the back surface and flush with all edges. The headboards are covered with a 2-in.-thick slab of foam rubber, then with material of your choice.

The beds, which are mounted on top of the 8-in.-high platform, are ¾-in.-thick plywood, hinged to an extension as shown in the diagram. Around the edges of this platform is a ½x2-in. solid wood strip to keep the 4-in. foam rubber mattress from sliding off.

The leg of the bed is exactly 8 in. high, to match the platform at the headboard. The leg is made of two pieces of ¾-in. plywood, mounted on top of each other, to lend extra strength. The leg is mounted to the bed with 8-in. folding brackets. When folded up, the bed is held in place with a 6-in. brass latch.

To cover the bed area, two-door folding door sets are mounted to each end of the built-in which in this case is against the wall. They were made of ¾-in. Novoply, and mounted with No. 2520 Grant Folding Door hardware.

After the doors fit perfectly, they are covered with Nakora V-Plank paneling to match the rest of the room.

Since the Nakora paneling is already prefinished for you, a light waxing is really all that is necessary to finish your work. If this type of paneling is not used, paint or stain will enter into your plans to some extent.

The next and final step in your job involves upholstering the beds and their headboards with foam rubber cushioning and any fabric which suits your fancy. Hardware is optional. •——*by Bill Baker*

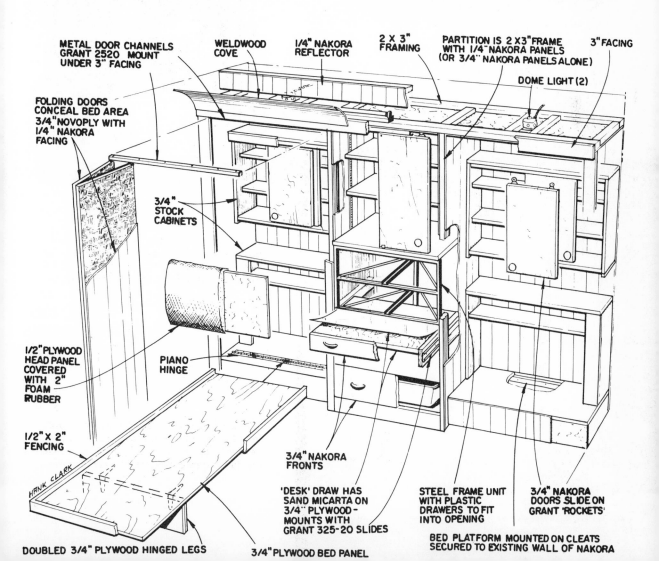

METAL DOOR CHANNELS GRANT 2520 MOUNT UNDER 3" FACING

WELDWOOD COVE

1/4" NAKORA REFLECTOR

2 X 3" FRAMING

PARTITION IS 2 X 3" FRAME WITH 1/4" NAKORA PANELS (OR 3/4" NAKORA PANELS ALONE)

3" FACING

DOME LIGHT (2)

FOLDING DOORS CONCEAL BED AREA 3/4" NOVOPLY WITH 1/4" NAKORA FACING

3/4" STOCK CABINETS

1/2" PLYWOOD HEAD PANEL COVERED WITH 2" FOAM RUBBER

PIANO HINGE

1/2" X 2" FENCING

HANK CLARK

DOUBLED 3/4" PLYWOOD HINGED LEGS

3/4" PLYWOOD BED PANEL

3/4" NAKORA FRONTS

'DESK' DRAW HAS SAND MICARTA ON 3/4" PLYWOOD - MOUNTS WITH GRANT 325-20 SLIDES

STEEL FRAME UNIT WITH PLASTIC DRAWERS TO FIT INTO OPENING

3/4" NAKORA DOORS SLIDE ON GRANT 'ROCKETS'

BED PLATFORM MOUNTED ON CLEATS SECURED TO EXISTING WALL OF NAKORA

Units of the center were built separately and then assembled. Lazy susan will store more than 300 disks, and it is turned by small electric motor.

"Before" photo shows the design problem that faced the author. Shallow areas before the ducts were used to house the twin stereo speakers, over 8' apart.

Basement Music Center

A component stereo system, television, and generous tape and disk storage are included in this installation. It can be built into just 9 feet of wall space

IF you have 14 feet of wall space in your basement, you can duplicate this project. If you have only 9 feet of wall space, you can still duplicate the music center itself.

The music center consists of two stereo speaker enclosures; a TV-hi-fi unit with record turntable and changer, a tape recorder and a tape storage drawer; an enclosure for tuner and stereo amplifier; and a vent cutout—all very well condensed.

The television receiver is mounted on a platform which, with the help of No. 325 Grant slides, can be brought out of the wall to its full depth. A lazy-susan bracket then makes it possible to turn the TV in the desired direction.

Next to the music center proper is lazy-susan disk storage for better than 300 records. It is mounted on a slow-turning window-display motor that enables you to make your selection by merely pushing a button to put the lazy susan in motion.

With the speakers over 8 feet apart for perfect listening, with unimpeded viewing, and the Fleetwood television remotely con-

trolled from chairside, you have a lazy man's paradise in your basement.

Though the installation, as pictured, takes up over 18 feet, much room was left for built-in storage—for such things as folding chairs, tables, etc.—and are not part of the basic project.

The walls and the ceiling were first furred out—2x3's for the walls and 1x2's for the ceiling. Due to the fact that this basement had beams running across with air ducts mounted next to them, it was necessary to box these two sections in, dropping the ceilings in those areas. In order to beautify these drop ceilings, indirect lighting was installed. This was done by widening the drop ceilings 8 inches on each side, mounting fluorescent strips on each side and then covering the visible front edges with a return strip wide enough to cover the entire fluorescent strip. Depending on the height of the drop ceiling an opening has to be left for the lighting to protrude beyond the front strip into the ceiling. The top of the fluorescent bulb should not be lower than 5 inches from the

Wall was furred out using 2x3's and all extending parts were boxed in. Ceiling followed and then electrical outlets were planned and placed.

Walls and partitions were then covered with ¼" prefinished Nakora V-plank paneling. Ceilings are of 12" Armstrong textured Cushiontone tiles.

ceiling at the very most, otherwise elevation blocks have to be mounted in order to lift the fixtures.

After all the structural work has been completed, the walls, if they are exterior walls, are covered with polyethylene on top of the 2x3's. The walls are then covered with prefinished 4x8 sheets of Nakora V-Plank paneling. Next, as shown in the diagram, the units are built as different cabinets, each completely finished, then installed in place and tied to the one next to it with screws from the inside. It is very important that all units line up perfectly in front and are plumb and level.

In this case, the upper front part of the built-in section was brought out to the desired overall depth of the built-ins. All front edges of the built-ins were brought up flush with this upper part, which is empty and unused.

Before paneling the upper section, ¾-inch Novoply folding door panels were cut and mounted with No. 2520 Grant folding door hardware. Once these doors work properly and fit snugly, and it is evident that the upper part of the built-in section

For unobstructed view, TV is on 4"-high platform equipped with lazy-susan bracket, installed with No. 325 Grant slides that permit complete extension.

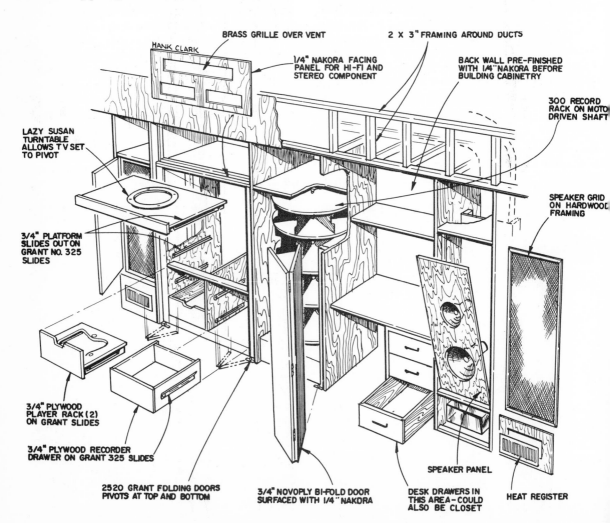

HANK CLARK

BRASS GRILLE OVER VENT

2 X 3" FRAMING AROUND DUCTS

1/4" NAKORA FACING PANEL FOR HI-FI AND STEREO COMPONENT

BACK WALL PRE-FINISHED WITH 1/4" NAKORA BEFORE BUILDING CABINETRY

300 RECORD RACK ON MOTO DRIVEN SHAFT

LAZY SUSAN TURNTABLE ALLOWS T V SET TO PIVOT

SPEAKER GRID ON HARDWOOD FRAMING

3/4" PLATFORM SLIDES OUT ON GRANT NO. 325 SLIDES

3/4" PLYWOOD PLAYER RACK (2) ON GRANT SLIDES

3/4" PLYWOOD RECORDER DRAWER ON GRANT 325 SLIDES

2520 GRANT FOLDING DOORS PIVOTS AT TOP AND BOTTOM

3/4" NOVOPLY BI-FOLD DOOR SURFACED WITH 1/4" NAKORA

SPEAKER PANEL

DESK DRAWERS IN THIS AREA – COULD ALSO BE CLOSET

HEAT REGISTER

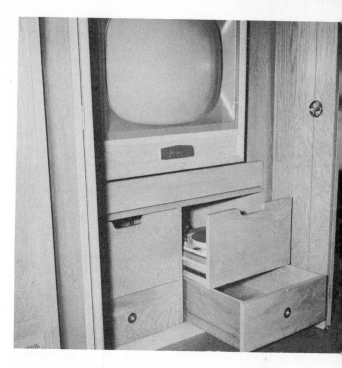

Similar slides greatly enhance accessibility of the tape recorder that is in one of the four drawers beneath the remotely-controlled Fleetwood TV.

Others of the four drawers house turntable and changer, provide storage for tapes, accessory gear. Tuner, etc., are above the TV receiver.

This 4'-wide section of the 15' built-in wall remains unused. It can be utilized for the storage of large objects such as cushions, tables, etc., or even a foldaway miniature train.

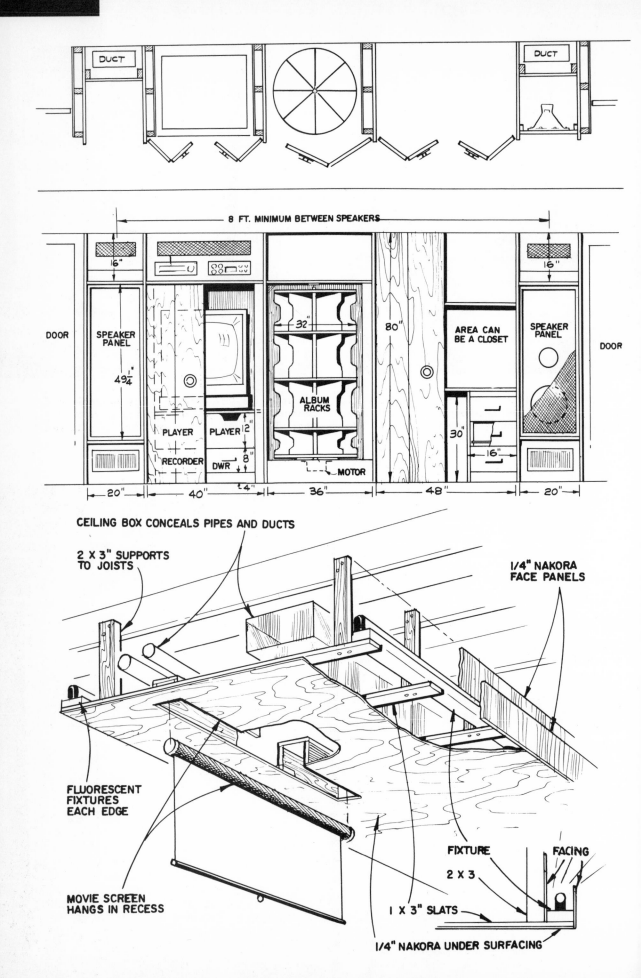

DUCT

DUCT

8 FT. MINIMUM BETWEEN SPEAKERS

16"

16"

DOOR

SPEAKER
PANEL

32"

80"

AREA CAN
BE A CLOSET

SPEAKER
PANEL

DOOR

$49\frac{1}{4}"$

ALBUM
RACKS

30"

PLAYER

PLAYER 12"

8"

RECORDER

DWR

16"

MOTOR

20"

40"

4"

36"

48"

20"

CEILING BOX CONCEALS PIPES AND DUCTS

2 X 3" SUPPORTS
TO JOISTS

1/4" NAKORA
FACE PANELS

FLUORESCENT
FIXTURES
EACH EDGE

FIXTURE

FACING

2 X 3

MOVIE SCREEN
HANGS IN RECESS

1 X 3" SLATS

1/4" NAKORA UNDER SURFACING

Above, note the five feet of speaker cabinet housing the stereo and hi-fi sound units. The preamp and tuner are above the television set.

Upper right, the separate unit across the doorway area but in line with the music center, is used for storage of small tables, chairs, games.

Right, all doors closed on the unit give the appearance of a solid paneled wall. Paneling was finished with ¼", V-plank prefinished Nakora.

is perfectly in line with the folding doors, the entire front is paneled with 4x8 prefinished V-plank Nakora paneling. Panels are first applied temporarily, then cut apart where necessary and permanently mounted with dabs of glue and finishing nails, just as if applied to a wall. Do not spread glue over entire surface of doors. It is important to make all parts fit perfectly so that the front of the built-ins look like a paneled wall.

Door pulls, about 3 inches in diameter, were mounted at regular doorknob height to the doors that need the most leverage to open. Good leverage can be obtained by mounting the pulls on the inner door 4 inches to center of pull, from the joint of both doors.

The two outside doors that cover the stereophonic speakers are mounted with piano hinges and held closed with magnetic catches.

Crown moldings are mounted where the front meets the ceiling, and base moldings are mounted up to the points where the doors are.

All partitions of the built-ins as well as ceiling and other exposed surfaces were made of ¾-inch Nakora plywood and finished to match the paneling. For economy, Novoply can be used successfully. Since all partitions will be covered with prefinished paneling, it is quite all right to use low-grade plywood sheeting just as long as the knot holes in your cheaper grade do not substantially lessen the strength of the partition. A good coat of wax on the prefinished paneling is all that's necessary for good looks. ●

by Bill Baker

Armstrong Cork Co.

Your young Jimmy 'Awkins and his pirate buddies would sure go for a basement bedroom like this. The focal point of the Treasure Island theme is a wood-barrel crow's nest. Sheet vinyl flooring of beach stones has an inset of a treasure island with a black pirate cross marking buried treasure.

Masonite Corp.

Ideas for Your Basement

Start with a theme, then use your imagination to create the image.

Neighbors would envy this basement recreation room. Woodgrain pegboard panels combine beauty with utility for holding sports gear.

Insulation Board Inst

No more washday blues. An efficient clothes care center like this could even be used for entertaining. Acoustical insulation board panels in the suspended ceiling absorb much of the noise generated by machines.

An easy project for the handyman is a basement workshop. Concrete slab supports heavy equipment.

Portland Cement Assn.

THOSE who've done it say it's best to plan your basement remodeling when you're far away from it—out at the beach or skiing, etc. When you are in your basement, it's too hard to picture it as anything but a cellar full of junk. In order to create ideas your mind must be loose.

One simple plan that gets you started effectively is to select a theme for your basement—such as Knights of the Round Table—and go from there.

Take these pages of ideas that others have used for rejuvenating their basements along with you to the fishing hole. You'll likely come back all fired up on a plan of your own. •

Armstrong Cork Co.

A home discotheque out of a grotty basement. The whole theme is go-go from top to bottom. Walls are done in bold stripes and paisley patterns with the stripes repeated in cushioned vinyl floor tile. The "cage" sets the theme immediately. Bar and record cabinet are tucked out of dance area.

There is nothing to be said for the basement at left. After remodeling, various family-living rooms, partly partitioned from each other, are made available for lounging and entertaining. The openness is carried to the stairway where it helps to make the whole basement more approachable.

Masonite Corp.

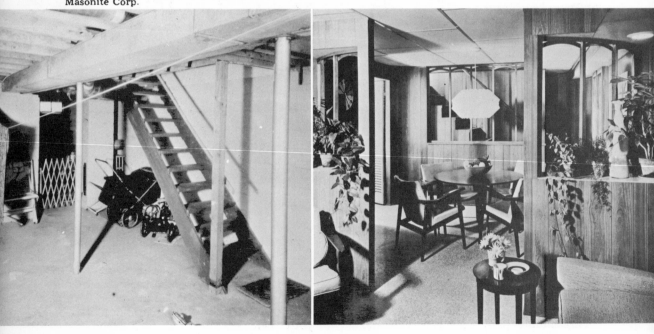

An attractive family room was made with little improvements. A plank ceiling was installed, block walls were painted and curtains and shutters on windows, plus some period furniture, make the room complete.

Portland Cement Assn.

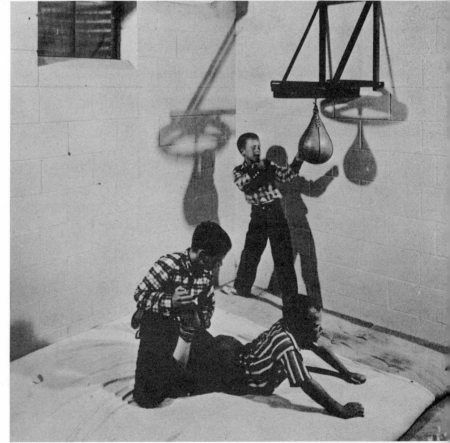

An easy weekend basement remodeling, consisting of painting the block walls and installation of a few recreational needs can be very inexpensive. Save up for full treatment later on.

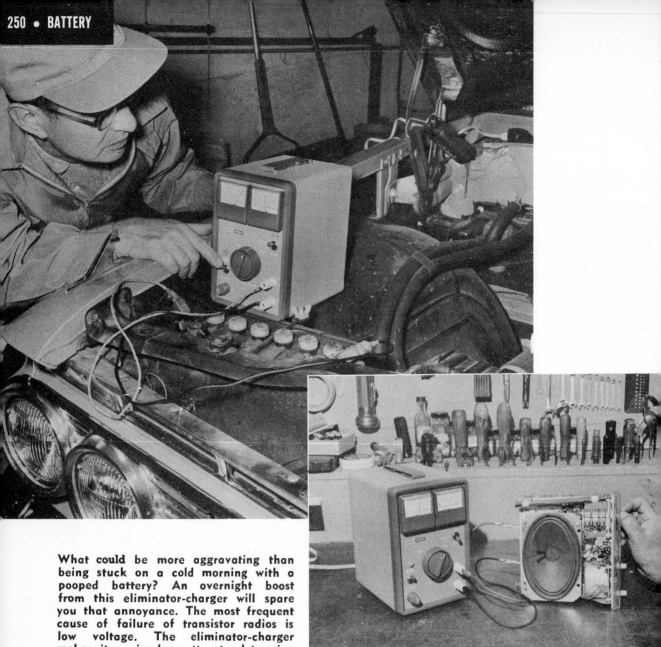

What could be more aggravating than being stuck on a cold morning with a pooped battery? An overnight boost from this eliminator-charger will spare you that annoyance. The most frequent cause of failure of transistor radios is low voltage. The eliminator-charger makes it a simple matter to determine if the set is bad or batteries are dead.

Battery Eliminator-Charger

FOR experimental and repair work on a variety of transistor equipment it is useful to have a dependable source of low-voltage DC other than conventional batteries. This source should be variable from zero to 15 or 16 volts and should be capable of delivering several amperes. If this current requirement sounds a bit high, remember that some amplifiers, transmitters and other devices draw quite a bit of juice from batteries.

At first glance you might think that an ordinary battery charger would be suitable for the job. Not so, since most chargers consist merely of a step-down transformer and a half-wave rectifier, their output current, while it flows in one direction is suitable for battery charging, produces a horrendous growl when applied to a receiver or amplifier.

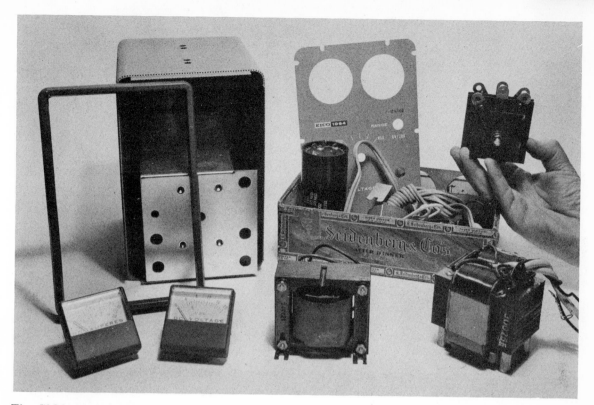

The EICO Model 1064 is simple to build and uses very few parts. In the foreground next to the meters are the filter choke (left) and power transformer (right). The rectifier stack is in hand.

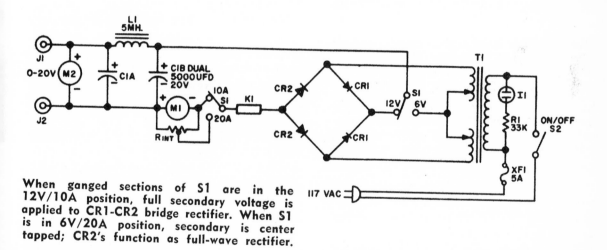

When ganged sections of S1 are in the 12V/10A position, full secondary voltage is applied to CR1-CR2 bridge rectifier. When S1 is in 6V/20A position, secondary is center tapped; CR2's function as full-wave rectifier.

The logical move is to add a brute-force filter between the rectifier and the output terminal to reduce the AC ripple to an acceptable minimum.

A well-filtered unit of this kind becomes a battery eliminator for bench use, but at the same time retains all its origina value as a charger for storage batteries. Fortunate indeed is the car owner with an unheated garage who has the foresight to give his battery a slow overnight boost during cold weather. In the morning he is rewarded with an instant start.

EICO recently introduced a well-designed and ruggedly constructed battery eliminator and charger that meets all the foregoing specifications. It's an easy kit project and can be completed in a couple of hours. As the schematic shows,

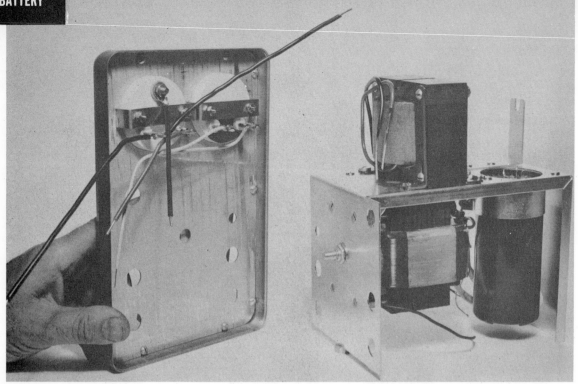

Transformer, choke, and the capacitor are on U-shaped chassis; meters mount on front panel.

it uses a step-down transformer (T1) with two secondary windings; the arrows on the latter represent contact arms controlled by the front panel knob marked VOLTAGE. Switch S1 permits choice of two output ranges, 0-8 volts at a maximum of 20 amperes, and 0-16 volts at 10 amperes. CR1 and CR2 are solid-state rectifiers. The filter consists of choke L1, (5 millihenries) and C1A-C1B, a dual capacitor, each section of which has the enormous value of 5,000 microfarads (five thousand, and no decimal point!). It's not difficult to produce this capacitance in electrolytics because the low operating voltage permits the use of thin chemical oxide films that act as the insulating separation between the plates; the closer the spacing of the plates, the higher the capacitance for the same area.

When line switch S2 is closed, voltmeter M2 monitors the output voltage continuously. The output current is shown on a dual-range ammeter, M1, which reads 0-10 and 0-20 amperes. The correct scale is selected when switch S1 (DPDT) is shifted to either its 6 or 12-volt position.

Double protection against overloading is furnished by the primary line fuse XF1 and thermal-overload breaker K1.

The latter opens just above 20 amperes, and resets itself when the overload is removed. I1 in the primary circuit of T1 is a neon pilot lamp.

The meters that come with the kit read a little on the high side, but still they are guides as to what is happening at the output.

Anyone who uses an eliminator of this kind certainly possesses a VOM or a VTVM, which can be connected quickly to check the voltage. If the voltage to a transistor device is correct (and some small receivers and transmitters can be quite fussy), the current will take care of itself. As a matter of fact, the current drain of portable receivers and 100-milliwatt license-free CB transceivers is so low that the ammeter on the panel of the eliminator doesn't even budge.

If the output voltage is reduced when the load is small, you will notice that the voltmeter does not respond instantly. This, of course, is due to the large value of the filter capacitors which necessarily discharge slowly since there isn't a bleeder resistor in the circuit to discharge them.

The EICO Model 1064 measures 10½ by 7¾ by 8¾ inches and is highly recommended as a shop accessory. Other models are available on the market.

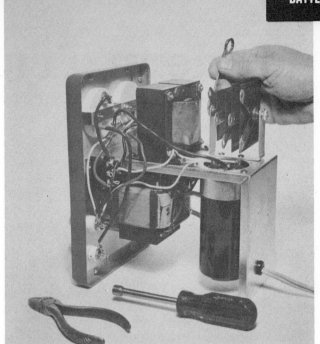

Right: With the panel and the chassis joined, the rectifier is mounted at the end of chassis above the filter capacitor. Below: The overload relay is fastened directly to one terminal of the rectifier stack. Rectifier gets warm, but open-mesh cabinet provides good ventilation.

Modern Trundle Bed

A TRUNDLE BED is traditionally a great space-saver. This modern version is especially suitable for a child's room. It keeps a second bed, hidden, completely made up for immediate use, protected from being torn up by children at play.

The basis of the project is a pair of steel folding cots—one a 36-inch cot and the other 30 inches—of the coil-spring type, with legs removed. Ball casters let the lower cot slide out of the upper so easily that a small child can handle it.

We used Philippine mahogany to make the trundle-bed frame, although any hardwood (with plywood to match) will do. For a finish, we simply applied three coats of water-white lacquer.

The tenons on the four 8-inch wide boards are 1 inch long. You make them ½ inch thick by removing ⅛ inch of stock from top and bottom. Then, you make them 7¾ inches wide by removing ⅛ inch of stock from each edge. The tenons at each end of the ¾x4x32½-inch boards are also 1 inch long, ½ inch thick, and are made 3¾ inches wide by removing ⅛ inch of stock from each edge.

MATERIALS NEEDED

For sides:

Four pieces of lumber, 1¼x2¾x22 in.

Two strips of lumber 1¼x2¼x77½ in.

Two strips of lumber ¾x1¼x77½ in.

Two boards ¾x8x74 in.

Two ¼-in. plywood panels (to match the lumber), 22¼x72½ in.

For ends:

Four pieces of lumber 1¼x4x22 in.

Two boards ¾x4x32½ in. (one trimmed to 30½ in.)

Two strips of lumber ¾x1¼x38½ in.

Two boards ¾x8x32½ in.

Two ¼ in. plywood panels (to match lumber) 22¼x31 in.

Frame for lower cot:

Four pieces of lumber, 1¼x1¾x14 in. (one end of each cut off at 45° angle)

One strip of lumber, 1¼x1¾x30½ in.

One strip of lumber, 1¼x1¾x31 in.

General:

Two folding steel cots (a 36 in. and a 30 in.), coil-spring type

Six 1-in. ball casters

Sixteen ⅜x2 in. carriage bolts

Eight 2½-in. No. 12 flathead screws

Eight 2-in. No. 12 flathead screws

Thirty-six 1¼-in. No. 8 flathead screws

Twenty 2½-in. No. 12 ovalhead nickel-plated screws

Glue

Water-white lacquer

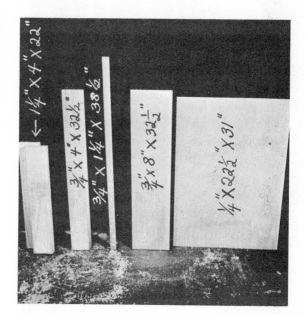

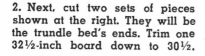
2. Next, cut two sets of pieces shown at the right. They will be the trundle bed's ends. Trim one 32½-inch board down to 30½.

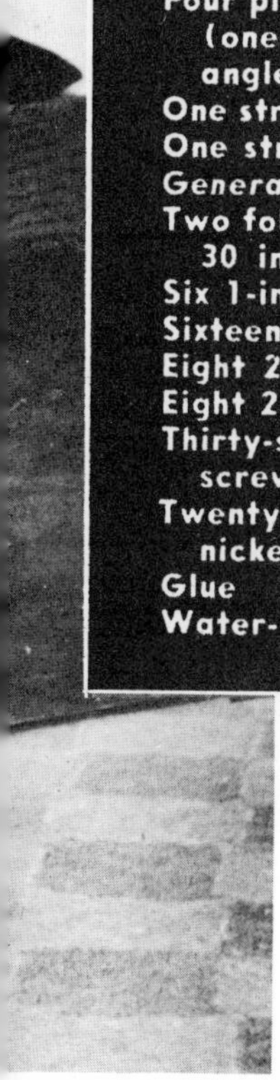

When plowing your grooves (Photos 4 and 5) in 38½-inch strips, be sure to stop the grooves about 2 inches from the ends of the pieces.

In two of the 1¼x4x22-inch boards, make mortises to fit the narrower tenons, opposite the mortises cut in Photo 6. (See Photo 6 for positioning of mortises.)

After removing the legs from the cots, clamp one 8x74-inch board to the springs (Photo 8), flush with the bottom of the rail and equidistant from its ends. After you've marked the rivet holes, counterbore them on the board to take carriage bolts.

When you've dropped the bolts into their holes and spread glue on the upper surfaces of the long pieces and the grooves of the side-panel assembly slip the 72½-inch plywood panel into the groove at one end, and then snap it into the groove at the other end (Photo 14). Let excess of ¼ inch of panel's width stick out beyond the board containing the bolts. Repeat this with the other assembly, then clamp them and let the glue set.

Taking four strips grooved in Photo 5, mark for holes about 1½ inches from each end of each board and at about 6-inch in-

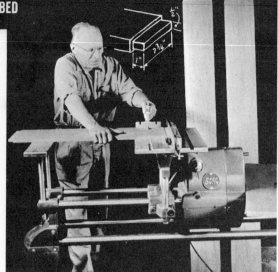

3. Cut a tenon at each end of the four 8-in.-wide boards. Do the same with ¾x4x32½-in. pieces.

4. Plow ¼x¼-in. groove in one edge of all eight 22-inch-long pieces. It is to be ¼ inch from edge.

5. Make the same cut in two of ¾x1¼x77½-in. strips and two ¾x1¼x38½-in. strips, as shown.

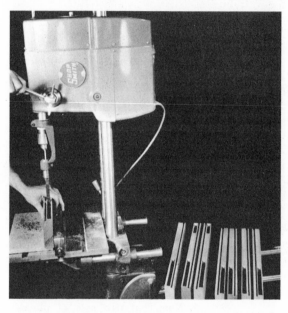

6. Mortise pieces of Photo 4 to fit 7¾-in. tenons. In 2 wider pieces, mortise opposite ends, too.

7. Remove the folding legs from springs of each cot. Simplest way is to grind off the rivets.

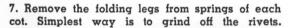

8. Clamp one of long 8-in. boards to the springs. Mark position of rivet holes (two at each end).

9. Counterbore marked points ¼ in.; drill through with ⅜-in. bit. Repeat on other similar board.

10. To each end of these, fit one of mortised 2¾-in.-wide pieces with glue. Note bolt holes.

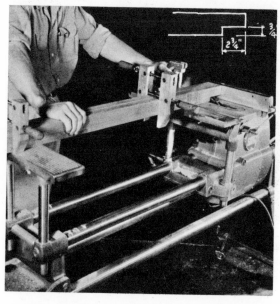

11. Make notches at each end of 1¼x2¼x77½-in. pieces. Notches are ¾ in. deep, 2¾ in. long.

12. On the reverse side of the notches, drill and countersink for a pair of 2½-inch No. 12 screws.

14. Put bolts in holes. Glue plywood panels to upper surfaces and into grooves of both assemblies.

13. Fasten notched pieces to assemblies of Photo 10. Fasten to faces farthest from ¼-in. grooves.

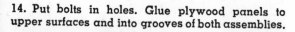

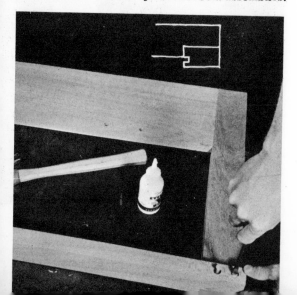

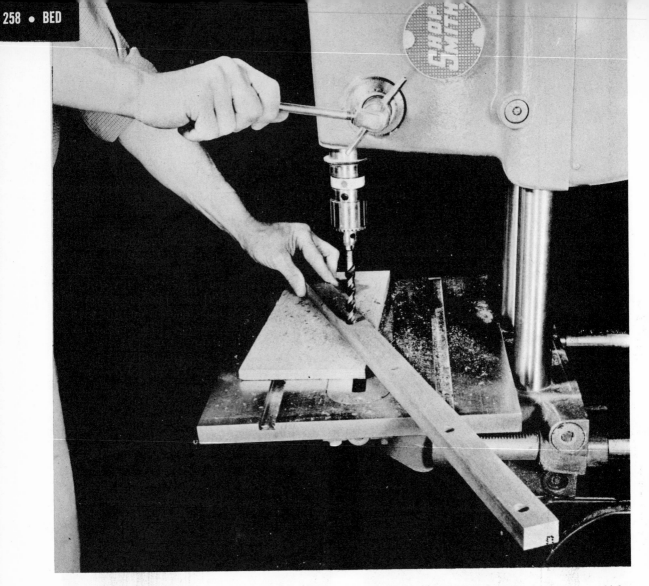

15. Now take four strips plowed in Photo 5. With grooved sides down, drill and counterbore for 1¼-in. No. 8 screws. Center the holes at the edges of the board and groove. Drill at about 6-in. intervals.

16. Put glue on plywood lip and fit to grooves of long pieces just drilled. Fasten them with screws.

17. Cover screws with plugs. Bolt panels to 36-in. bed frame as shown. Bolts are already in panels.

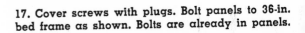

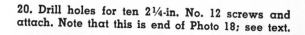

18. The next step in making the trundle bed is to assemble the ends one of which is seen here, glued and clamped. Refer to the text for component parts of each. The difference between the two is slight.

19. Onto each end panel, glue one of the grooved pieces. Fasten with screws. Cover screw-heads.

20. Drill holes for ten 2¼-in. No. 12 screws and attach. Note that this is end of Photo 18; see text.

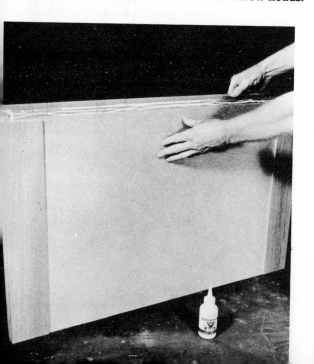

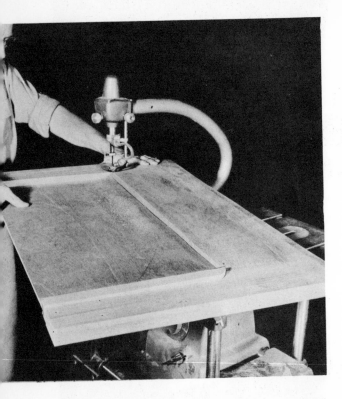

21. From second end, cut out curving sector as per text. Attach remainder to sides as in Photo 20.

22. These pieces frame lower bed. An end of 14-in. pieces is 45°; 30½-in. board, center has been cut.

tervals in between. Place these holes centered within the space between the edge of the boards and the grooves. Drill and counterbore these holes to take 1¼-inch No. 8 screws and ½-inch wood caps.

Assembling the Ends

The end panel shown in Photo 18 consists of an 8-inch wide tenoned piece, the 4-inch wide tenoned piece, the two pieces having two mortises each, and one of the 31-inch plywood panels. These have been glued and clamped, as shown. The second end panel is similar, with the exception that it does not use a 4-inch wide piece, and its side boards have but one mortise.

After you've glued a grooved piece onto each end panel, drill holes for screws as shown in Photo 20 (this applies to the *first* end panel you assembled). In attaching the end panel to the side panels (Photo

23. A 1-in.-diameter hole is centered 3½ inches from square end of each 14-in. piece for casters.

24. Next, center same-size holes in each end of the 31-in. piece. These are also for the ball casters.

20), do NOT use glue if you wish to keep the bed detachable for moving purposes.

From the second end panel (the one without the 4-inch wide piece), cut a section as shown in Photo 21. The section is cut on a line that removes 1¼ inches of the two side pieces, and curves to go along the line where the plywood meets the 8-inch wide board. After you've cut out this section, fasten the remaining part of the end panel to the other end of the side panels, just as you did in Photo 20.

Frame for Lower Cot

One end of each of the four 14-inch pieces for this assembly is cut off at a 45° angle, as seen in Photo 23.

The 1-inch holes which are bored 3½ inches from the square end of each 14-inch piece are meant to take ball casters. Note (in Photo 23) that holes in two pieces must be drilled in opposite sides from the holes

you drill in the other 14-inch pieces.

Before assembling the three pieces shown in Photo 25, mark and drill holes for bolts as indicated in the picture. Also, cut dadoes in the 31-inch piece so the assembly will fit on the end of the 30-inch bed frame, as shown in Photo 28. Be sure to make slots, such as the one seen in the upper right corner of Photo 25, so that the wood will fit over the iron of the bed.

Assemble another frame for the other end of the bed, similar to the one made in Photo 25. Fit it to the bed frame in the same way. When it is assembled, glue and dowel the ¾x4x30½-inch board to it, as shown in Photo 26. Then, glue this frame to the section cut from the end panel in Photo 21.

Bolt each frame to its end of the 30-inch cot, as demonstrated in Photo 28. Slide the lower bed into the frame supporting the upper bed. •

25. Assemble these pieces, dadoing 31-in. piece to fit bed (see Photo 28). Drill for bolts first.

27. Glue the frame just made to the panel cut from the bed end in Photo 21, as shown above.

26. Mount casters on first frame; assemble second and fit it to bed. Dowel 4x30½-in. piece to it.

28. Bolt each frame to its end of bed. Slide the lower bed into upper; end shown here goes in first.

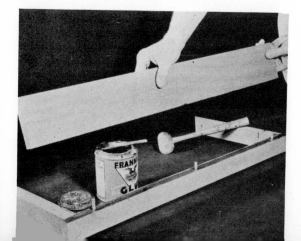

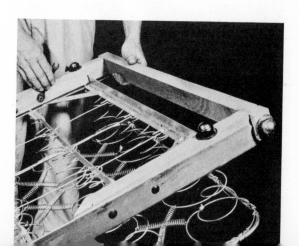

Built-In Baby Bed

Gate folds down or comes off altogether, depending on need. Drawer beneath is ample for all bedding.

Made of less than one sheet of hardwood plywood and a few solid pieces of lumber, it takes any standard mattress, offers some very special features

A BUILT-IN bed such as this one has several advantages. Not only is it relatively inexpensive, being built of less than one sheet of hardwood plywood and a few pieces of solid lumber, but it affords several features not found in conventional styles and designs. The front sections or gate can be completely removed for ease in handling the mattress and a large storage drawer directly underneath will hold all needed bedding and accessories. Nor is this bed permanently built in so that it can-

not be removed without destroying the walls. Two long lag screws and a few flat-headed wood screws anchor the bed to the walls and can be removed for eventual replacement with a bed more suitable for a growing child.

The bed is of conventional size, 27x51 inches, which permits the use of any manufactured spring or foam-rubber mattress. The distance from the floor to the top of the mattress is twenty-one inches which allows the baby to be handled without excessive bending and strain. These measurements, of course, can be altered to suit the needs of the builder.

The wood selected for this bed is Weldwood Samara, an African hardwood made into plywood by the U. S. Plywood Corporation, and is available at any lumberyard. An even less-expensive bed could be easily built to the same plan from ordinary fir plywood and stained and coated with Satinlac or merely enameled in a suitable color. The Samara plywood shown was finished with four coats of Satinlac, steelwooled, and then rubbed down with paste wax.

Begin to make this bed by building a frame of 2x3s on which the mattress will rest. Make the outside measurements of the frame exactly the size of the mattress, in this case 27x51 inches.

Miter the corners of the 2x3s and then cut notches for the half-lap joints by which the legs are attached to the frame. Cut the legs next so that they will fit tightly into the notches. Use a quick-setting glue such as Presto-Set and a few finishing nails to hold the legs in place. Saw some corner blocks next and, after checking the frame for squareness with a large carpenter's square, glue and nail the corner blocks underneath the frame. This will add considerable strength and rigidity to the bed.

The frame can then be anchored to the walls in the corner it is to occupy. Drill a

pilot hole in one side and one end of the frame and through the plaster into the studding. Use long lag screws in these two holes. Tighten them into the studding with a wrench.

Sawing the piece which forms the end of the bed is an easy matter, particularly if a saber saw is available. If such a saw is not available, the curved design at the corner can be changed to a straight line and cut with a hand saw or a table saw. Cutting the opening in the end piece is done by first drilling a hole at each corner of the rectangle large enough to receive the saw blade. Use a saber saw, keyhole type, hand saw, or a large jig saw.

The spokes in the end piece are cut from solid wood and are three quarters of an inch square. Dowel rods could be used but that would entail extra finishing. If a solid matching wood is used (mahogany in this case), no extra finishing is required. Simply sand away all of the sharp corners on the squares and attach them with short quarter-inch dowels and glue. Mark the top edge of the end piece and the bottom edge of the large opening to locate the spokes. Drill quarter-inch holes completely through the top section of the end piece so that the top dowel rods can be driven into the spokes from the top edge.

Apply glue to the dowel rods and also to the holes before driving them into place. If a quick setting glue is used, the entire

The bed frame can be anchored to the wall at any point with long lag screws. Aim for stud base.   **This L-shaped piece of aluminum permits the two front sections to slide. Drill only through metal.**

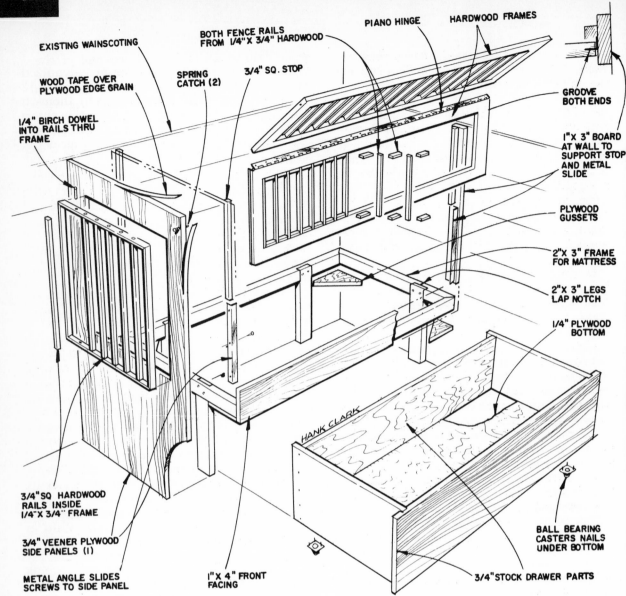

EXISTING WAINSCOTING

WOOD TAPE OVER PLYWOOD EDGE GRAIN

1/4" BIRCH DOWEL INTO RAILS THRU FRAME

SPRING CATCH (2)

3/4" SQ. STOP

BOTH FENCE RAILS FROM 1/4" X 3/4" HARDWOOD

PIANO HINGE

HARDWOOD FRAMES

GROOVE BOTH ENDS

1"x 3" BOARD AT WALL TO SUPPORT STOP AND METAL SLIDE

PLYWOOD GUSSETS

2"x 3" FRAME FOR MATTRESS

2"x 3" LEGS LAP NOTCH

1/4" PLYWOOD BOTTOM

HANK CLARK

BALL BEARING CASTERS NAILS UNDER BOTTOM

3/4" STOCK DRAWER PARTS

3/4"SQ HARDWOOD RAILS INSIDE 1/4"X 3/4" FRAME

3/4" VEENER PLYWOOD SIDE PANELS (1)

METAL ANGLE SLIDES SCREWS TO SIDE PANEL

1"X 4" FRONT FACING

end piece will be ready to attach to the bed frame in less than one hour. Note that the inside edge of the opening in the end piece should be framed either with four long solid strips or covered with Weldwood wood tape and contact cement. This is more easily done before the spokes are attached but can be done afterward if desired.

Cut the long front piece which covers the front rail of the bed frame at this point. Make it 6 inches wide and exactly 51 inches long. Glue and clamp it to the front rail of the frame. If no clamps are available, use some long finishing nails placed as inconspicuously as possible. Set them deeply into the plywood with a nail set. These holes can be puttied over, filled with glue and wood dust or, after finishing, filled with matching wood Putty-Stik.

Attach a strip of wood to the wall next at the right-hand side of the bed. This strip

will serve to anchor the front sections or gates to the wall. Also at this time cut the solid wood squares or the quarter-round molding which will be screwed to the wall on both sides of the end piece at the other wall. These two pieces will serve to hold the end of the bed tightly in position. Attach the end piece to the bed frame with glue and finishing nails before screwing the molding to both sides of the end piece.

Cover the exposed edges of the plywood with either solid wood strips or Weldwood wood tape. If wood tape is used, coat both the edge of the plywood and the back of the tape with two coats of Weldwood contact cement. Allow this cement to dry to the touch before pressing the tape into position on the edge. Then use a roller or the smooth handle of a file or other tool to press the tape into final contact with the edge. File the excess tape away and lightly sand the corners of the edges with some fine sand-paper.

Saw out the two gates or front sections from adjacent spots on the sheet of ply-wood. These can be sawed on any radial arm or table saw. The inside opening in each of these pieces is easiest cut with a saber saw or large jig saw. Drill blade holes in each corner first, of course. Cut the spokes for these pieces from ¾-inch solid stock. Make the spokes a quarter inch thick. Sand away all of the sharp corners either before or after attaching them to the opening. Dowel rods may be substituted here, too, but again that calls for an extra finishing job. If solid spokes of ¾-inch stock are used, they should be cut so as to fit tightly in the opening between short spacers of the same size stock. Glue and nail each piece into position starting at one end of the opening and working toward the opposite end. Drive the small finishing nails (¾-inch) into the top and bottom ends of each spoke so that the nail heads will be covered by the short spacers between the spokes. Sand sharp corners off the edges of the spacers, too. Use 1½-inch-wide piano hinge between the two gates of front sec-tions. Place the two sections in a wood vise and screw the open hinge into place on both pieces at the same time.

Now saw a kerf in the two ends of the bottom section. Saw this kerf at least ¾ of an inch deep. This is the kerf which slides over the metal angles attached to the wall and the end of the bed and permits the front sections to be removed from the bed entirely.

The two metal angles can be cut from a scrap piece of aluminum or of galvanized iron. Make them 1½ inches wide and 12 inches long. With a mallet, bend them in the middle ninety degrees over the sharp edge of a block of wood. Drill three holes in each of these L-shaped metal pieces the size of the shank of the screws to be used. Make the three screws which attach the metal piece to the head of the bed long enough to go through the wood strip and into the wall itself.

Two round spring-type catches are used to hold the upper gate in the closed posi-tion. Drill holes for these catches in the opposite ends of the top gate and screw a striking plate in place to hold the bolt in the closed position. These plates can also be made from a scrap of aluminum or brass. Use two screws on each plate.

Finish the entire bed with four coats of Satinlac. Rub down the first coat with ei-ther steel wool or fine sandpaper. Apply the remaining three coats and steel wool again. Weldwood paste wax can then be used to give a final protective coat.

When the baby decides he needs more room to carouse, the crib can be removed from the wall, the holes filled with wood putty, and you are ready to begin looking for plans to build a youth-bed to take its place. A bit of imagination on your part will probably give you a good notion of how you can extend this design to conform to the requirements of a youth-bed spring and mattress. A slightly larger frame is really all that is necessary plus a few alterations on the top design. In any event, you've got two to three years to figure it out. ●——by Bill Moore

End piece has section removed to allow air to circulate. Fill in with dowel rods or spokes.

Four ball-type casters are fastened to the bot-tom of the drawer for easier sliding; hammer on.

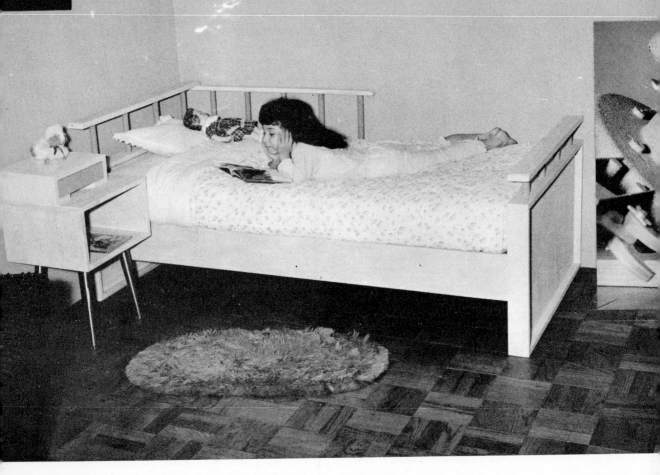

Without the left side rail, bed becomes reading-and-sleeping area for the older child.

Youth Bed   By Bill Baker

Decorative, long-lasting and versatile, this bed attracts children.

THIS attractive and clean-lined modern bed will easily serve your youngster from the age of 3 through his teens. It can be built very inexpensively and will last, without the repairs needed for a less well-designed piece.

The model bed was built from ¾-in. Nakora Plywood and solid wood, and finished with white Firzite painted on and carefully rubbed off to show the beautiful grain of Nakora. The dowels were painted pink and the color scheme made the bed extremely attractive.

From a 4x6- or 4x7-foot sheet of ¾-in. Nakora Plywood, cut out all pieces shown in the drawings. Next, square up all the pieces, making the edges smooth.

Cut 26 feet of ¾x2¾-in. strips from solid wood. Miter these strips around both the head and footboards and temporarily tack them onto the edges. Then number them for future replacing. In the short pieces, in the exact center of the width, bore four equally spaced ½-in. holes ⁵⁄₁₆ in. deep; then drill ³⁄₁₆-in. holes all the way through. Start the holes 1½ in. from each end. In the longer pieces, bore five equally spaced holes the same way. Mount all pieces, with the exception of the top strip, using glue and 1¼-in. No. 8 flathead screws. Make sure that equal amounts extend on each side.

Before mounting the top strip, cut the decorative top rails to the same size as this top strip. Then place them side by side and, in the exact center of the

Solid wood trim for head and footboard is cut to 45-degree angle for the mitered corner.

Bore ½-in. holes to depth of 5/16 in. in edges, then drill 3/16-in. holes through these.

Mark holes for 1-in. dowels by aligning top rail of head and footboard with top edges.

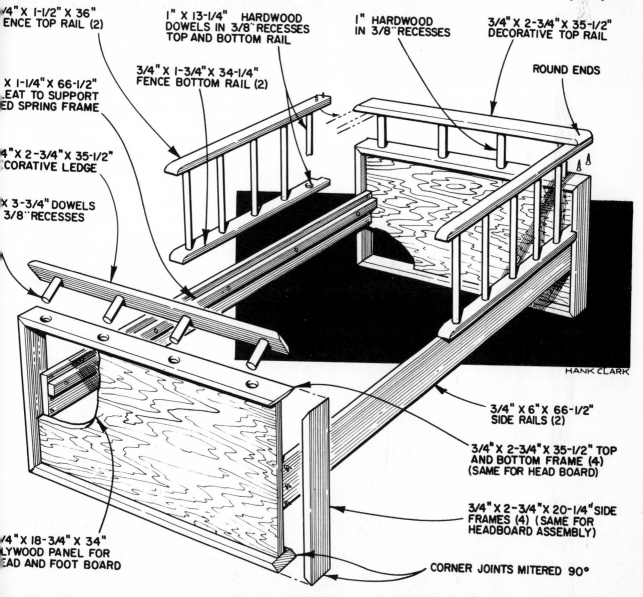

/4" X 1-1/2" X 36"
ENCE TOP RAIL (2)

1" X 13-1/4" HARDWOOD DOWELS IN 3/8" RECESSES TOP AND BOTTOM RAIL

1" HARDWOOD IN 3/8" RECESSES

3/4" X 2-3/4" X 35-1/2" DECORATIVE TOP RAIL

3/4" X 1-3/4" X 34-1/4" FENCE BOTTOM RAIL (2)

ROUND ENDS

X 1-1/4" X 66-1/2" EAT TO SUPPORT ED SPRING FRAME

4" X 2-3/4" X 35-1/2" CORATIVE LEDGE

X 3-3/4" DOWELS 3/8" RECESSES

HANK CLARK

3/4" X 6" X 66-1/2" SIDE RAILS (2)

3/4" X 2-3/4" X 35-1/2" TOP AND BOTTOM FRAME (4) (SAME FOR HEAD BOARD)

3/4" X 2-3/4" X 20-1/4" SIDE FRAMES (4) (SAME FOR HEADBOARD ASSEMBLY)

/4" X 18-3/4" X 34" LYWOOD PANEL FOR EAD AND FOOT BOARD

CORNER JOINTS MITERED 90°

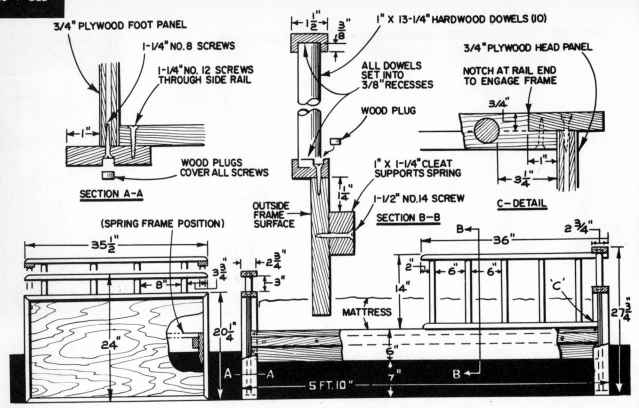

3/4" PLYWOOD FOOT PANEL

1-1/4" NO. 8 SCREWS

1-1/4" NO. 12 SCREWS THROUGH SIDE RAIL

WOOD PLUGS COVER ALL SCREWS

SECTION A-A

1" X 13-1/4" HARDWOOD DOWELS (10)

ALL DOWELS SET INTO 3/8" RECESSES

WOOD PLUG

1" X 1-1/4" CLEAT SUPPORTS SPRING

1-1/2" NO.14 SCREW

OUTSIDE FRAME SURFACE

SECTION B-B

3/4" PLYWOOD HEAD PANEL

NOTCH AT RAIL END TO ENGAGE FRAME

C—DETAIL

(SPRING FRAME POSITION)

35½"

8"

3¾"

24"

20¼"

2¾"

3"

MATTRESS

5 FT. 10"

36"

2¾"

2"

6"

6"

14"

6"

7"

27¾"

width, mark them for 1-in. holes for dowels. For the location of the holes, see the drawings.

Next, on the top surface of the top strips and the bottom surface of the decorative top rails, bore 1-in. holes (or holes as nearly as possible the same size as the dowels you purchased, since 1-in. dowels are not always exactly 1 in. in diameter).

Mount the top strip in place, using glue and 1¼-in. No. 8 flathead screws. Repeat the same procedure on the bottom and top rail strips of the side rails, as was done for the head and footboard strips. Refer to the drawings here. In

the exact center of the 1-in. holes, bore ⅜-in. holes ⅜ in. deep. Also bore ⅜-in. holes about ¾ in. deep in the center of both ends of each 1-in. dowel. This is done, of course, after the dowels are cut to their required length as shown in the drawings. Glue ⅜-in. dowels into the ends of the 1-in. dowels, leaving ⁵⁄₁₆ in. extend out.

After sanding the edges of head and footboards, as well as rounding the decorative top rail and sanding the 1-in. dowels, mount the shorter decorative top-piece to the footboard, and the higher top-piece to the headboard. Use glue, and carefully square up the

One-in. holes are bored ⅜ in. deep in top edge of the head and footboard as well as in top rail (ledge), for dowels. Bore similar holes in the top and bottom fence rails. Drill ⅜-in. holes ⅜ in. deep in center of each.

Mount all solid-wood edge pieces around head and footboards with glue and screws.

Matching long-grain wood plugs are glued into the ½-in. holes to cover screw heads.

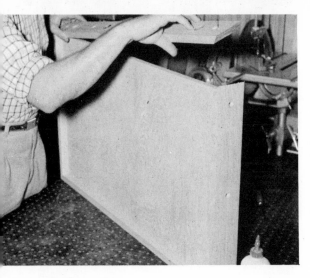

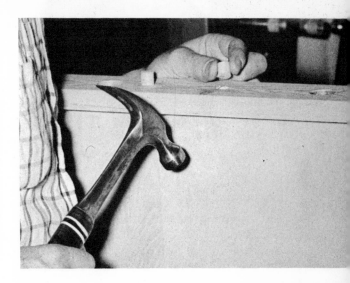

Ends of the top rail strips are rounded on disk sander to complete quarter round.

Dowels have been glued into top ledge and this assembly is then glued to footboard.

Solid wood strip is glued, screwed to inside of side rails, 1¼ in. from top edge.

Top edges of the side rails are covered by strip of Weldwood Flexible Wood-Trim.

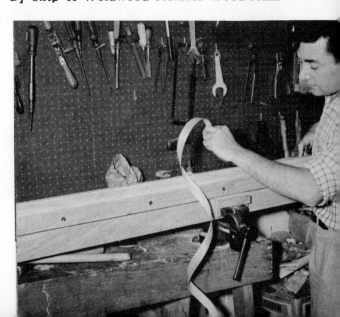

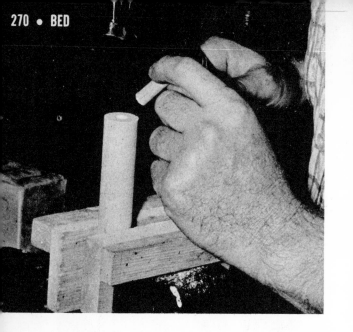

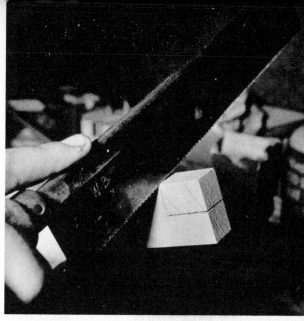

In center of all 1-in. wood dowels, ⅜-in. dowels are glued tightly into both ends.

Bottom fence rails are notched ¾x1 in. to fit against side edges at head, foot.

Left-hand fence is assembled with glue and clamped. Note notch at end of bottom rail.

Above, rails are mounted 7 in. from bottom with screws. Corner angles are added.

Below, fences are fastened to rails with four 1¼-in. roundhead screws and washers.

dowels; then set them aside to dry. Make the bed rails by first mounting the solid wood spring support 1¼ in. from and parallel with the top edge, using glue and 1¼-in. No. 14 flathead screws. Cover the top edge with matching Weldwood Wood-Trim.

One-half inch from each end of each bed rail, bore three equally spaced ¼-in. holes. Countersink these for flathead screws on the inside of the bed rails. Start the holes ¾ in. from top and bottom edges. Now assemble the side rails, using glue and wood clamps. Make sure that the dowels are squared up before setting aside.

Next, mount the bed rails to the head and footboards, 7 in. from the bottom. Use 1¼-in. No. 14 flathead screws. For additional support, 3-in. iron angles should be placed beneath the spring support strip. Use no glue for the final assembly.

When mounting the side rails, first hold them snugly against the headboard, then fasten the top rail strip to the bottom surface of the decorative headboard strip. Use 1¼-in. No. 8 roundhead screws but, again, no glue. Finally, the side rails are fastened to the bed rails with 1¼-in. No. 8 roundhead screws and washers. •

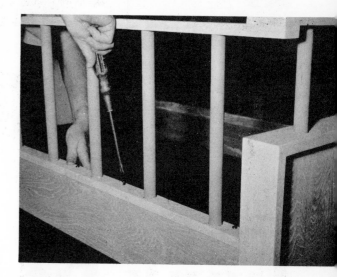

Top strip of fence is fastened to bottom of headboard ledge; keep back edge flush.

Bunk Bed

Ladderless "over-and-under" sleeps two children in comfort and privacy ... a simple project in plywood.

FAMILY growing? House remaining the same size? Not enough bedrooms for everyone? The over-and-under or double bunk bed is an obvious means of accommodating two children in the same floor space previously occupied by one.

In the bunk bed shown on these pages, the usual ladder has been eliminated. The plywood end piece and the two sides are both perforated with an organized pattern of holes of rectangular shape. These holes provide all the foot space a child needs for getting into or out of the upper bed. Incidentally, they add to the decor and also give better ventilation than permitted by solid boards.

Double bunk bed is free standing and requires no fastening to wall.
One-foot overhang at top keeps a restless sleeper from tumbling out.

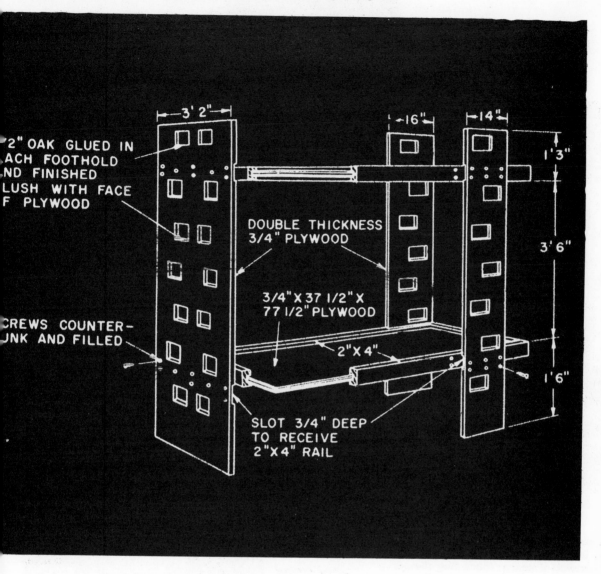

2" OAK GLUED IN
ACH FOOTHOLD
ND FINISHED
LUSH WITH FACE
F PLYWOOD

DOUBLE THICKNESS
3/4" PLYWOOD

3/4" X 37 1/2" X
77 1/2" PLYWOOD

CREWS COUNTER-
UNK AND FILLED

2" X 4"

SLOT 3/4" DEEP
TO RECEIVE
2" X 4" RAIL

3' 2"

16"

14"

1'3"

3'6"

1'6"

The construction is as simple as it is ingenious. It is also very strong, and will withstand any punishment a couple of vigorous youngsters are likely to inflict on it. The structure is completely free-standing, and unlike many other designs does not have to be fastened to the wall. As family requirements change, it can be shifted around.

Cut and finish all pieces in the shop and then assemble them in the bedroom. Finish with a non-toxic paint in colors to match the rest of the furnishings.

Note particularly that the footholds are reinforced by ½-inch strips of oak (or any other scraps of hard wood) on their bottom edges. These are needed, not primarily to withstand wear (although they help in this respect), but to protect the bare feet of the occupants from splinters. An ideal tool for cutting the footholds is one of the new power-operated saber saws.

Foam rubber slabs make good mattresses. The bunks are big enough to accommodate children in comfort even when they are no longer children but fully grown hulks of college age.

As many children like to read in bed, provide individual lamps for the bunks. One occupant can sleep while the other reads, because the top bed acts as a shield for the lights.

The vertical spacing between the two bunks depends to some extent on the ceiling height. In most rooms this is 8 feet, and the dimensions in the drawing are adjusted for it. If it is much lower, bring the upper bunk down accordingly.

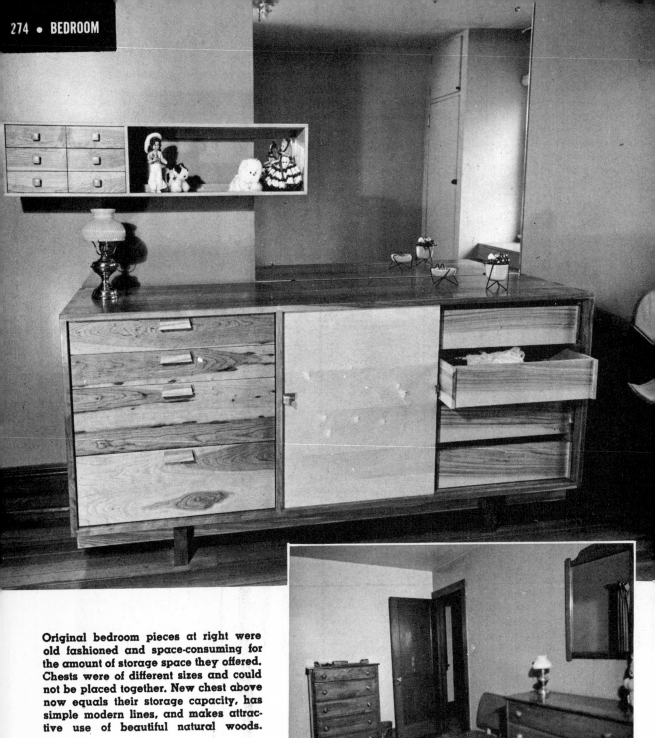

Original bedroom pieces at right were old fashioned and space-consuming for the amount of storage space they offered. Chests were of different sizes and could not be placed together. New chest above now equals their storage capacity, has simple modern lines, and makes attractive use of beautiful natural woods.

Modern Bedroom Suite

Text and Photos by Hal Kelly

Build your own bedroom furnishings to fit your special needs. Here are step-by-step instructions for chest, bed, and shelf construction.

Plank edges are first evened with a jointer-planer. Hold-down rollers aid the craftsman working alone.

HAVE you priced any of the nice simple bedroom suites now available? Have you looked at those with clean functional design, pleasing choice of beautiful, matched woods, and then added the cost of having each piece custom-finished to your special size requirements? When you do you are likely to decide, as I did, that you will want to build these pieces yourself.

This entire set can cost you under $300.00, including a six-inch-thick foam rubber mattress and a four-foot-square mirror. It was carefully designed, and fine woods were used—mostly cherry and poplar, with touches of ash for strength. This is no depression project constructed from apple crates; choice of fine fruit woods, carefully selected, can give you examples of very attractive grain without breaking your budget. Over 100 hours of work are required, but you will be rewarded with 21 storage drawers, one of which holds over 9½ cubic feet, plus a money savings of

Planed planks are now glued and clamped together. Sapwood grain has been carefully matched.

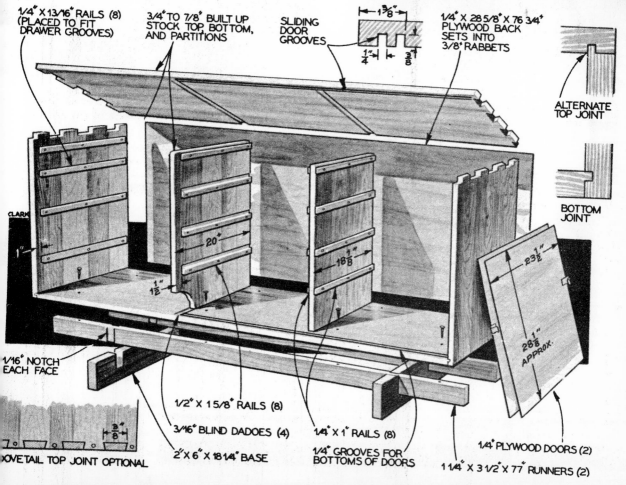

1/4" X 13/16" RAILS (8) (PLACED TO FIT DRAWER GROOVES)

3/4" TO 7/8" BUILT UP STOCK TOP, BOTTOM, AND PARTITIONS

SLIDING DOOR GROOVES

1 3/8"

1/4"   3/8"

1/4" X 28 5/8" X 76 3/4" PLYWOOD BACK SETS INTO 3/8" RABBETS

ALTERNATE TOP JOINT

BOTTOM JOINT

CLARK

1"

20"

1 1/2"

18 1/8"

23 1/2"

28 1/8" APPROX.

1/16" NOTCH EACH FACE

3/8"

DOVETAIL TOP JOINT OPTIONAL

1/2" X 1 5/8" RAILS (8)

3/16" BLIND DADOES (4)

2" X 6" X 18 1/4" BASE

1/4" X 1" RAILS (8)

1/4" GROOVES FOR BOTTOMS OF DOORS

1/4" PLYWOOD DOORS (2)

1 1/4" X 3 1/2" X 77" RUNNERS (2)

Prepare a guide block for getting correct angle when cutting dovetails. Back saw rides against it.

A router, set into a drill press adapter, cuts out back of slot. Corners are cleared with file, chisel.

Exposed dovetails make functionally attractive as well as strong joints, but take time and patience.

Dado and rabbet joints are glued, screwed, and plugged at bottom; can also be used for top joints.

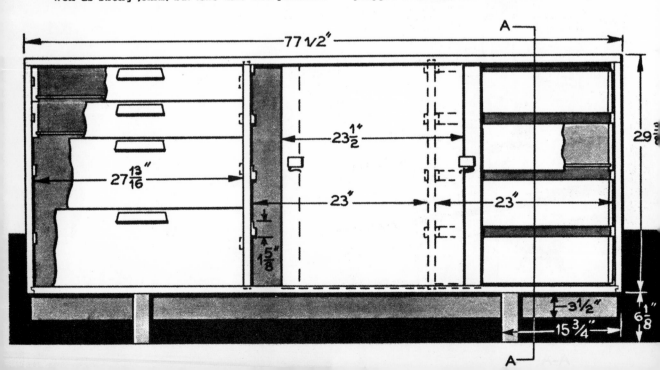

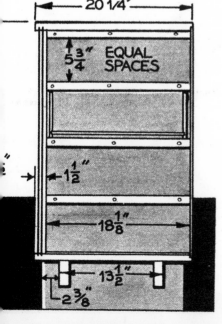

Here a belt sander smooths off plugged screw holes, excess dried glue, and any unevenness of joints.

Corner of chest at bottom joint is chiseled out to complete rabbet for the inset of the plywood back.

perhaps $700, and a suite fitting your needs.

Working with fine woods takes no longer than with the cheapest. Though I might have saved $50 on the whole project with low cost lumber, I also considered the value of my time, and of fine wood that would last. I chose cherry as a stable wood which takes a fine finish and is nice to work with. I would no more stain this great wood than I would use house paint on a new Cadillac —the wood, in aging, will take on a golden cherry color. I also chose sapwood, with its creamy white, for accents on drawer fronts.

This six and one-half foot chest is a monster for storage capacity. First glue up wood for the top, bottom, sides, ends, and dividers. Cut to size, make all the dadoes, rabbets, and dovetails, and then assemble. Consult the drawings for all measurements. Simpler joints, as illustrated, may be substituted for the dovetails at the top of the chest, but I found after practicing on some

Structural base, above, is assembled from long ash runners carefully fitted and glued into cherry base pieces. Interior of chest is shown below. Guides at right are L-shaped to keep drawers from rubbing.

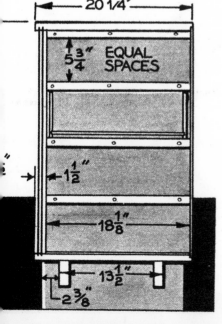

20 1/4"

5 3/4" EQUAL SPACES

1 1/2"

18 1/8"

13 1/2"

2 3/8"

A-A

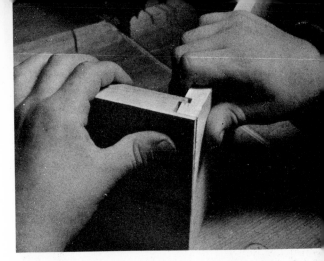

Grooved joint on corners of exposed drawers is made with two dado cuts. Set piece in simple jig.

Close up of locking joint for exposed drawers is shown. Front piece for drawer is at left of photo.

Stack up drawer sides so that similar cuts can be run through at same time. Radial arm saw helps.

scraps that I had no trouble. Both sets of dovetails took a total of four hours and their strength and beauty make them well worth the trouble.

Measure your bedroom's dimensions and plan the over-all size of your chest to fit your room's proportions. Complete first the frame of this cabinet. Drawers can then be made to fit.

Build the four exposed drawers first. The fronts were made from ¾-inch cherry, the sides and backs from ½-inch poplar. Before assembly, cut dadoes in the side pieces

The details and dimensions of exposed drawers are diagramed below. Note small sliding inner drawer.

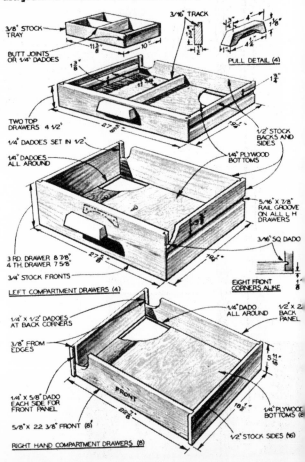

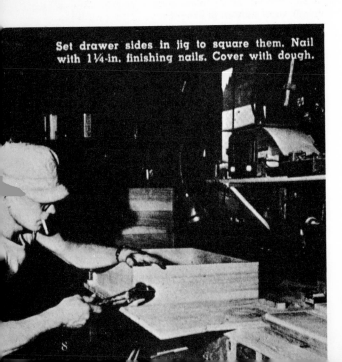

Set drawer sides in jig to square them. Nail with 1¼-in. finishing nails. Cover with dough.

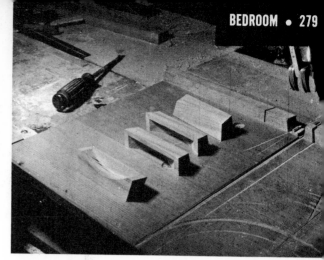

Finger recesses are cut easily and safely from a single strip. Dado cutter makes hollows quickly.

After finger pulls are cut, handles are separated. Total time for custom pulls will be only half hour.

for the drawers to slide on. A simple jig is a big time saver for squaring them up.

Next you make the eight English-type drawers. These are all the same size, with ⅝-inch ash used for the front and ½-inch poplar for the sides and back. Once again I would suggest a jig for squaring up the drawers as you assemble them.

The base is also of simple, functional design. On 2x6-inch cherry base pieces are fitted ash runners. The whole unit was sprayed inside and out with Fabulon and rubbed down with No. 0 steel wool. •

Molded plywood handles for sliding doors are made from four thin pieces glued and clamped.

Small sliding "false teeth" drawer inside one or more of the larger drawers makes an attractive custom touch. Details for it are shown in construction diagram.

The molded handles which were glued up and clamped into shape are now fastened on the sliding doors, and the doors installed over the English drawers, completing the chest.

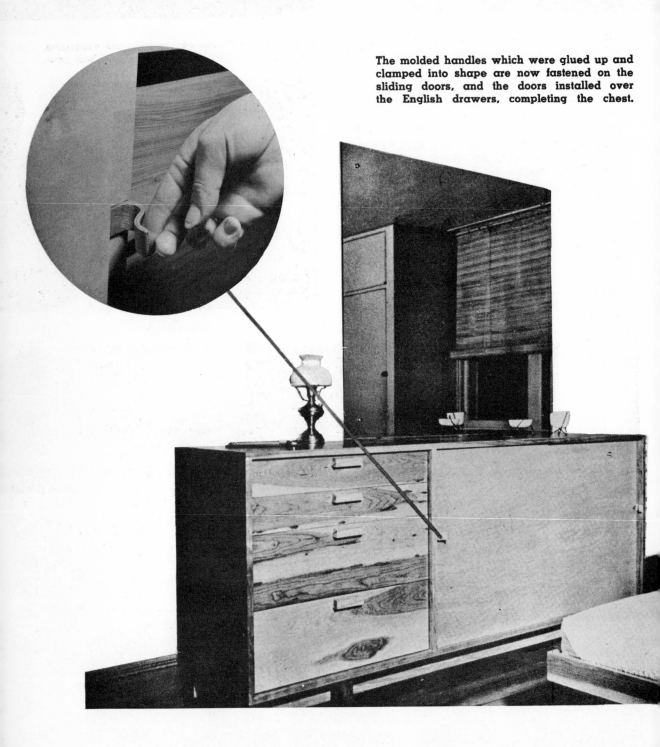

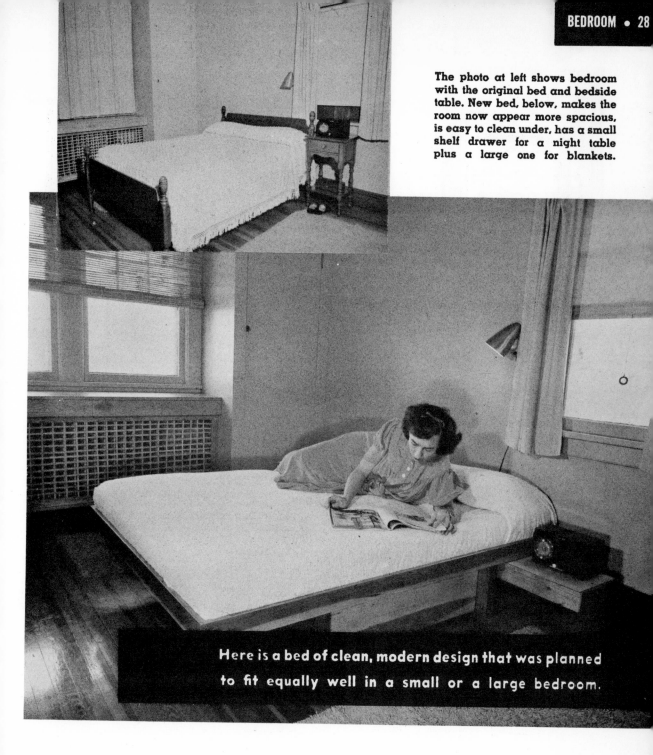

The photo at left shows bedroom with the original bed and bedside table. New bed, below, makes the room now appear more spacious, is easy to clean under, has a small shelf drawer for a night table plus a large one for blankets.

Here is a bed of clean, modern design that was planned to fit equally well in a small or a large bedroom.

PLEASING functional design, comfort, and extra storage space are incorporated in this bed. Raised from the floor, it is easy to clean under, and unlike a conventional design, it does not seem to crowd a small room.

The bed frame is made of ash for strength; the ends are lap jointed and rabbets are run along both edges, one for the ½-inch plywood to set into, the other for the bed sides to slip over. The sides are made with a dado cut inside to fit the edge of the frame.

All ends of the sides are mitered at a 45-degree angle with two ends assembled with splines and glued and screwed together; the other two ends are screwed only. This makes for easy disassembly into two large L shapes when you move. After the unit is screwed to the legs, the plywood is screwed in place. Finish the bed to match chest. •

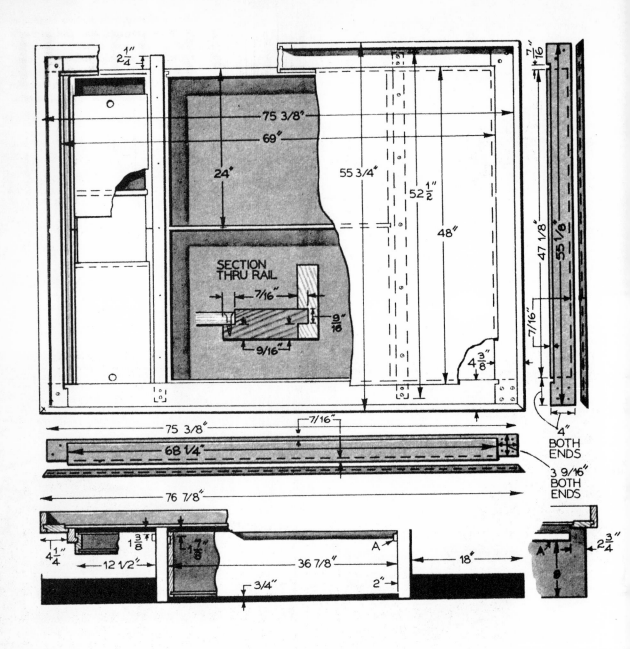

SECTION
THRU RAIL

Lap joints at ends of bed frame were made with
several passes of dado cutter on radial arm saw.

Finished lap is ready for glue and screws. Diagonal
opposites are screwed only for easy disassembly.

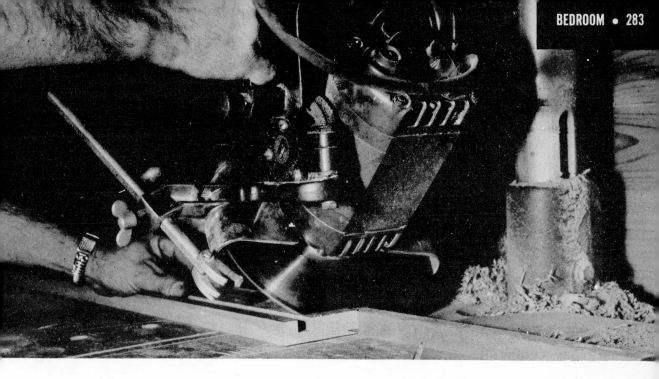

Dadoed side rails are mitered, top, then clamped together and slotted at rt. angle for a spline.

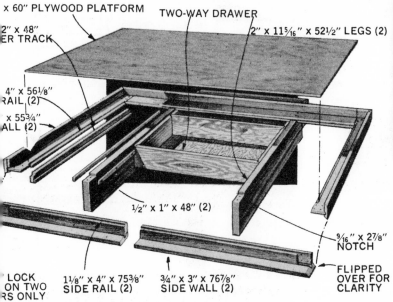

x 60" PLYWOOD PLATFORM

TWO-WAY DRAWER

2" x 11⁵⁄₁₆" x 52½" LEGS (2)

2" x 48"
ER TRACK

4" x 56⅛"
RAIL (2)

x 55¾"
ALL (2)

½" x 1" x 48" (2)

⁹⁄₁₆" x 2⅞"
NOTCH

FLIPPED
OVER FOR
CLARITY

LOCK
ON TWO
RS ONLY

1⅛" x 4" x 75⅜"
SIDE RAIL (2)

¾" x 3" x 76⅞"
SIDE WALL (2)

Corner, below, takes four screws but no glue and thus can be unscrewed, disassembled for moving.

Corner, lower left, shows line of the glued spline, added for extra strength in corners that are glued.

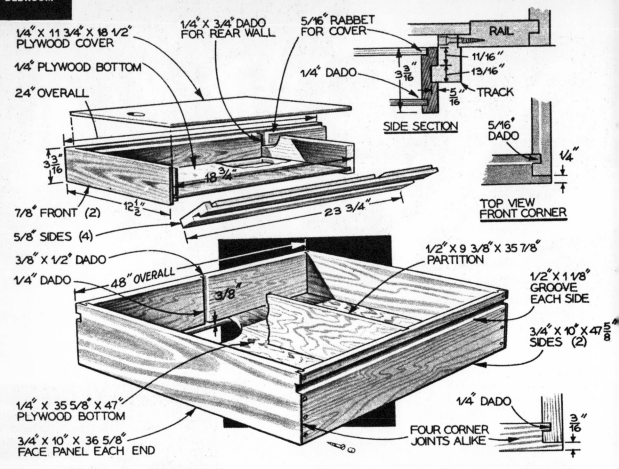

1/4" X 11 3/4" X 18 1/2" PLYWOOD COVER

1/4" PLYWOOD BOTTOM

24" OVERALL

1/4" X 3/4" DADO FOR REAR WALL

5/16" RABBET FOR COVER

1/4" DADO

RAIL

11/16"

13/16"

3 3/16"

5/16"

TRACK

SIDE SECTION

3 3/16"

18 3/4"

7/8" FRONT (2)

12 1/2"

5/8" SIDES (4)

23 3/4"

5/16" DADO

1/4"

TOP VIEW FRONT CORNER

3/8" X 1/2" DADO

1/4" DADO

48" OVERALL

3/8"

1/2" X 9 3/8" X 35 7/8" PARTITION

1/2" X 1 1/8" GROOVE EACH SIDE

3/4" X 10" X 47 5/8" SIDES (2)

1/4" X 35 5/8" X 47" PLYWOOD BOTTOM

3/4" X 10" X 36 5/8" FACE PANEL EACH END

1/4" DADO

FOUR CORNER JOINTS ALIKE

3/16"

The combination night table and drawer, diagramed upper left, is shown being assembled.

After being completely glued and screwed together, night table drawer is shown drying while clamped.

Photo, below, shows small shelf drawer at upper right (note sliding cover), large drawer closed.

Here is the bed completed. The large drawer under the bed pulls out for 12 sq. ft. of storage space.

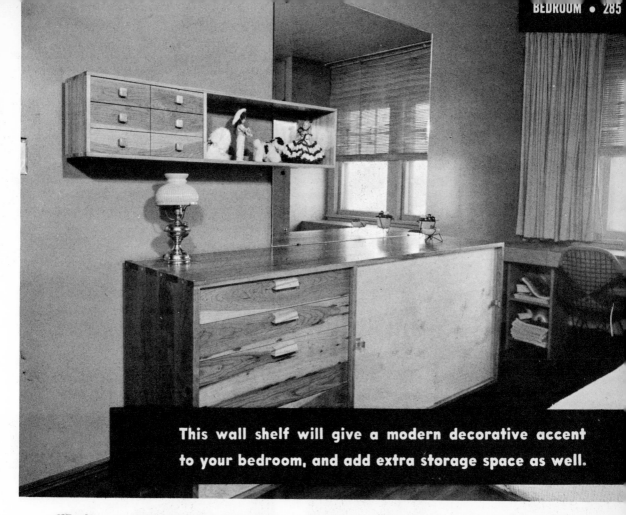

This wall shelf will give a modern decorative accent to your bedroom, and add extra storage space as well.

Whether you make the large chests or this small shelf first, one will be practice for the other. The building details of joints and drawers, as shown below, are the same.

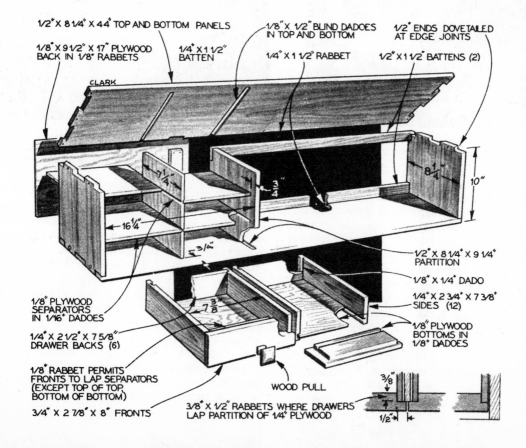

1/2" X 8 1/4" X 44" TOP AND BOTTOM PANELS

1/8" X 1/2" BLIND DADOES IN TOP AND BOTTOM

1/2" ENDS DOVETAILED AT EDGE JOINTS

1/8" X 9 1/2" X 17" PLYWOOD BACK IN 1/8" RABBETS

1/4" X 1 1/2" BATTEN

1/4" X 1 1/2" RABBET

1/2" X 1 1/2" BATTENS (2)

CLARK

7 1/4"

8 1/4"

10"

16 1/4"

3/4"

1/2" X 8 1/4" X 9 1/4" PARTITION

1/8" X 1/4" DADO

1/4" X 2 3/4" X 7 3/8" SIDES (12)

7 3/8"

1/8" PLYWOOD BOTTOMS IN 1/8" DADOES

1/8" PLYWOOD SEPARATORS IN 1/16" DADOES

1/4" X 2 1/2" X 7 5/8" DRAWER BACKS (6)

1/8" RABBET PERMITS FRONTS TO LAP SEPARATORS (EXCEPT TOP OF TOP BOTTOM OF BOTTOM)

3/4" X 2 7/8" X 8" FRONTS

WOOD PULL

3/8" X 1/2" RABBETS WHERE DRAWERS LAP PARTITION OF 1/4" PLYWOOD

3/8"

1/2"

As with the chest, all sides of the shelf were dadoed and the corners dovetailed before assembly.

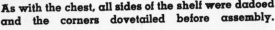

A small bayonet-type electric jig saw is handy for cutting dovetails. Make slow and careful cuts.

As with the chest, all sides of the shelf were dadoed and the corners dovetailed before assembly.

All available clamps, and then some, were used. Note clever center clamp improvised from a chain.

View from rear shows shelf before installation of plywood back. Vertical piece is screwed to wall.

THIS little wall cabinet can be the extra touch to give charm and individuality to your bedroom. With its six small drawers and display shelf it makes a handy way to keep the chest top below uncluttered and still store or show off attractive knickknacks, perfume bottles, etc.

The cabinet construction procedure is the same as the large chest. Frame and drawers are constructed of the same woods and sprayed or brushed with Fabulon, a finish I have found particularly durable. Sound your wall to locate a stud and screw your cabinet to it, placed so that it overlaps the mirror for a decorative accent.

Your only ready-made purchases to complete the suite will be your mirror and mattress. A ¼-inch-thick plate glass wall mirror, four by four feet, can be bought for about $40.00 with installation included. Since ordinary foam rubber I found too soft for comfort, I had 4½-inch regular foam cemented to a 1½-inch thickness of firmer rubber. U. S. Rubber Supply Co. of 8 West Broadway, New York City 7, can prepare this to order. A full size mattress and zippered cover came to about $85.00.

This project is well within the capabilities of any home craftsman—a bedroom suite at substantial savings. •

Drawer bottoms, like the back piece over the drawer section, are made from ⅛-in. plywood. These are slid into grooves and nailed to the back piece.

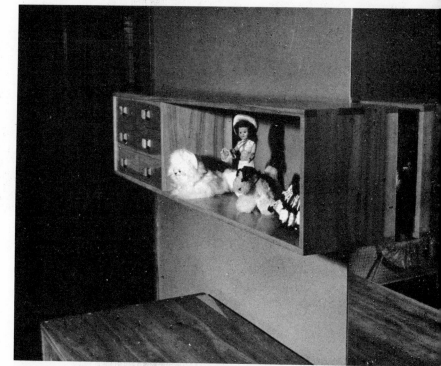

Here is the shelf installed. Knickknacks placed here can keep top of the chest clear. Note how contrasting wood plugs holes in shelf and chest.

These six drawers, though small, provide valuable storage compartments. Wood drawer pulls may be bought from local hardware stores.

modernize your child's bedroom

Text and Photos by Hal Kelly

Simple decorating changes and construction of these space-saving units can transform any child's room into a cheerful play area.

THE units shown on these pages were designed specifically for my eight-year-old son's bedroom. The new furniture replaced a bulky chest of drawers and an oversized secretary desk. Aside from the obvious visual improvement, the new pieces offered much more living and playing space in the small room and gave him about 40 per cent more storage space than he had before. Best of all, he'll never really outgrow any of these pieces; each of them will be as useful ten years from now as it is today.

While we were at it, we removed the old wallpaper and so-called decorative trim around the windows and doors. Then the wall and ceiling were painted a light buff. The window shades were replaced with a bamboo blind 6 ft. wide and 4½ ft. long attached to the ceiling. Since most bamboo shades are about 6 ft. in length, it was necessary to cut 1½ ft. or so from the length of each shade. Don't chuck away the excess slats—they'll come in handy later on. A ceiling traverse rod was installed for the wall-to-wall drapes.

Radiator Cover and Storage Unit: This handsome piece performs the double function of concealing an unattractive radiator, and at the same time embodies a great deal of storage space for toys, blankets, books, etc. The exact height and length will be dictated by the window height and size of your room.

Solid African mahogany, ¾ in. thick, was used throughout. The first procedure is to cut all the legs to size. Note that the two left members are 10¼ in. wide, the right members 12 in. wide. Next make appropriate cutouts for your baseboard and for the 1x2-in. cleat behind the top. If desired, the two right legs may be recessed at the bottoms to create a lighter effect. Make the required shelf dadoes in each leg, and recess for the wastebasket. At this time, also make dadoes in the right legs to accept the bamboo slats, as well as the dadoes for the hardboard back.

Dadoes and the right-hand rabbet are now cut into the top board, and the dado for the bamboo is cut in the top piece. Shelves are next cut to

These sets of "before and after" photos show the tremendous transformation that's possible even in a small room. Two bulky pieces of furniture, left, have been replaced by space-saving, handsome chest and desk, and unsightly radiator was cleverly hidden by a built-in cover which also includes plenty of storage.

First step in constructing radiator unit is to cut all four legs; make appropriate dadoes for shelves.

Mahogany plugs are glued into ⅜-in. counter-bored pilot holes, will be sanded flush later.

The built-in pivoting wastebasket, made of ½ and ¾-in. stock, is assembled with glue and nails.

Complete unit ready for sanding. Note cutouts in legs for baseboard, and position of Masonite back.

Belt sander does a quick, accurate job of sanding plugs. Those at left have already been smoothed.

For getting into tight areas, an oscillating sander is excellent. Blind dado is visible in leg at right.

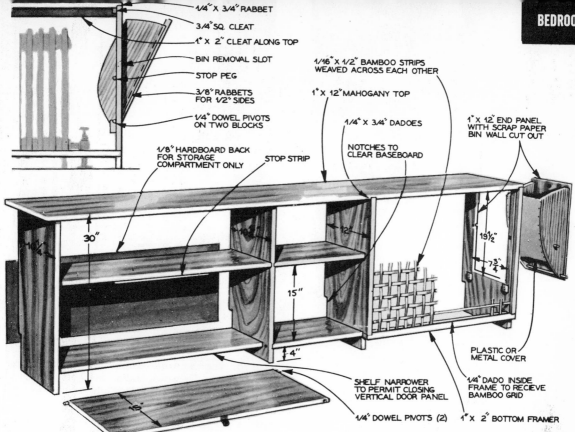

1/4" X 3/4" RABBET
3/4" SQ. CLEAT
1" X 2" CLEAT ALONG TOP
BIN REMOVAL SLOT
STOP PEG
3/8" RABBETS FOR 1/2" SIDES
1/4" DOWEL PIVOTS ON TWO BLOCKS
1/8" HARDBOARD BACK FOR STORAGE COMPARTMENT ONLY
STOP STRIP
1/16" X 1/2" BAMBOO STRIPS WEAVED ACROSS EACH OTHER
1" X 12" MAHOGANY TOP
1/4" X 3/4" DADOES
NOTCHES TO CLEAR BASEBOARD
1" X 12" END PANEL WITH SCRAP PAPER BIN WALL CUT OUT
30"
15"
4"
19 1/2"
7 3/4"
PLASTIC OR METAL COVER
SHELF NARROWER TO PERMIT CLOSING VERTICAL DOOR PANEL
1/4" DADO INSIDE FRAME TO RECIEVE BAMBOO GRID
1/4" DOWEL PIVOTS (2)
1" X 2" BOTTOM FRAMER

size. The entire unit was assembled with No. 7, 1¼-in. screws inserted into counterbored holes, which are later plugged with ⅜-in. mahogany plugs glued in place and sanded flush.

The built-in wastebasket is an extra little feature I added as a custom touch. Of course, it can be omitted if desired. The front panel of the basket utilizes the piece that was cut out of the right-hand leg. Sides are of ½-in. stock, and the back is plastic;

sheet metal may also be employed. The entire unit pivots on one long dowel along the bottom, which is 8¼ in. long, and two short dowel pins inserted as stops. Make appropriate cutouts in the leg recess and position basket in place. To remove, simply lift out and up.

Finally, the door is cut to size. A dowel pin about 1 in. long is inserted in the right-hand side. Bore a corresponding hole in the leg to the right of the door. Swing the door

Two short dowel pins on sides of wastebasket act as stops. Slanted notches are cut by hand. Unit pivots on a longer dowel engaged by two cleats.

Loosely woven bamboo slats fitted into four dadoes will hide radiator. Cut them a bit longer than necessary, then snip to exact size needed.

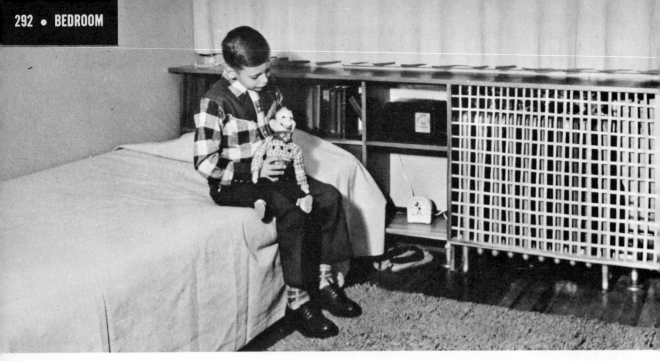

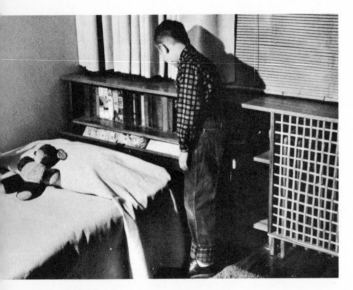

Above: The closed compartment is used for sheets and bedding, and is the only area that really requires a back. Below: The built-in wastebasket can be removed by pulling it out and then straight up.

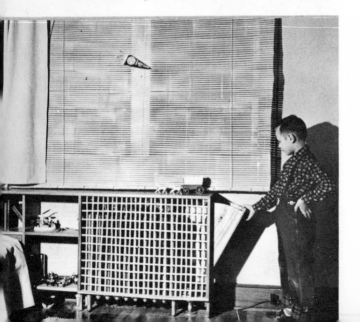

Above: The finished unit in use. Shelves offer ample space for clock, radio, and books. The radiator is hardly visible through bamboo screen.

into position, so that the dowel pin is engaged in the hole. Raise the door to the position it would normally be when closed, and drill a hole through the left-hand leg, letting your drill cut about 1 in. into the door itself. Simply drive a pin through the leg and into the door, and that's the works. If necessary, sand the pin flush with the leg surface. A bullet catch inserted in the center of the door will keep it firmly closed; a short leather strap acts as a pull.

Sand down the entire unit, and apply three coats of Fabulon or a similar natural finish. The leftover bamboo from the blind is now slipped into the ¼-in. dadoes. You'll note that they are woven in an open pattern and are spring-fitted into the dadoes. Cut the strips longer than necessary in order to compensate for the extra length used in the weaving process.

Chest of Drawers: You'll be amazed at the amount of household and bedroom appurtenances you'll be able to store away in these eight generous drawers. I was lucky enough to find mahogany up to 24 in. wide; of course the same width can be obtained by gluing up narrower lengths. The cabinet is 19 in. deep, 29 in. high, and 6½ ft. long.

Cut the top, sides, and dividers, dadoing and rabbeting the top and bottom to receive the respective dividers and ends. Also make rabbets for ⅛-in. hardboard back, and dadoes for the sliding doors where indicated. Make the top dado ⅜ in. deep and the bottom one $\frac{3}{16}$ in. deep. In this manner, the doors can be easily slipped into place

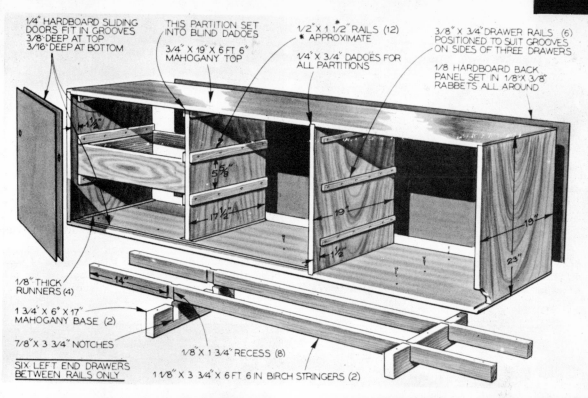

1/4" HARDBOARD SLIDING DOORS FIT IN GROOVES 3/8" DEEP AT TOP 3/16" DEEP AT BOTTOM

THIS PARTITION SET INTO BLIND DADOES

3/4" X 19" X 6 FT 6" MAHOGANY TOP

1/4" X 3/4" DADOES FOR ALL PARTITIONS

1/2" X 1 1/2" RAILS (12) * APPROXIMATE

3/8" X 3/4" DRAWER RAILS (6) POSITIONED TO SUIT GROOVES ON SIDES OF THREE DRAWERS

1/8" HARDBOARD BACK PANEL SET IN 1/8" X 3/8" RABBETS ALL AROUND

5 5/8"

17 1/2"

19"

1 1/2"

19"

23"

1/8" THICK RUNNERS (4)

1 3/4" X 6" X 17" MAHOGANY BASE (2)

7/8" X 3 3/4" NOTCHES

14"

1/8" X 1 3/4" RECESS (8)

1 1/8" X 3 3/4" X 6 FT 6 IN BIRCH STRINGERS (2)

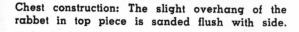

SIX LEFT END DRAWERS BETWEEN RAILS ONLY

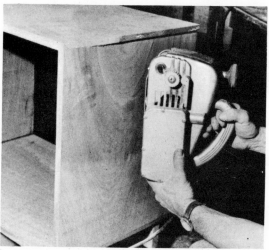

Chest construction: The slight overhang of the rabbet in top piece is sanded flush with side.

Closeup of one of the vertical dividers and twin dadoes that will accept Masonite sliding doors.

The elements of the six English-type drawers are cut and dadoed in a single time-saving operation. This 8-in. saw was the only one employed for all the units shown.

Base is comprised of two 78-in. lengths of 1⅛x3¾-in. birch stringers, and two 17-in. pieces of 1¾x6-in. mahogany. The base is inverted above.

Snug matching dadoes in all four members of the base obviate the necessity of a single screw or nail. Elements will fit firmly without fastenings.

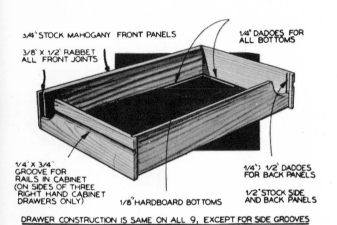

3/4" STOCK MAHOGANY FRONT PANELS

1/4" DADOES FOR ALL BOTTOMS

3/8" X 1/2" RABBET ALL FRONT JOINTS

1/4" X 3/4" GROOVE FOR RAILS IN CABINET (ON SIDES OF THREE RIGHT HAND CABINET DRAWERS ONLY)

1/4") 1/2" DADOES FOR BACK PANELS

1/2" STOCK SIDE AND BACK PANELS

1/8" HARDBOARD BOTTOMS

DRAWER CONSTRUCTION IS SAME ON ALL 9, EXCEPT FOR SIDE GROOVES

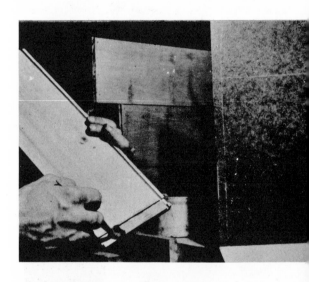

Above: Typical drawer construction. Right: Apply generous coat of glue before assembling drawers.

Clamp each drawer tightly, as shown, before nailing to assure drawers of uniform size and shape. Use scrap block to prevent marring wood.

Drawers should follow plans closely, so check them carefully for squareness. Assembly-line technique will cut down your work considerably.

Two upper sets of English-type drawers rest on 1½-in. rails, the bottom ones on ⅛-in. runners.

Three right-hand drawers have dadoes cut into their sides which engage these ⅜-in. splines.

by inserting them into the top dado, then letting them drop down into the bottom one. The basic frame is glued, screwed and plugged.

The base is very handsome, but easy to make. It is constructed of 1⅛-in. birch stringers and 1¾-in. mahogany baseboards. Not a single screw was used in this base. Instead, snug dadoes cut into each member retain the entire structure.

The component parts of the three big drawers which occupy the right-hand area are cut in one time-saving operation. Note the dadoes in the drawer sides, which will

engage the ⅜x¾-in. drawer rails. Rails are screwed to inside cabinet walls.

The six English-type drawers that occupy the remaining portion come next. All the members of these drawers should be cut and dadoed at the same time, then assembled. They are quite easy to install: each of the two bottom drawers rests on a pair of ⅛-in.-thick runners placed to prevent scratching of the cabinet floor. Position one bottom drawer, then place a $\frac{1}{16}$-in. shim on the top edges. Place the runners on top of the shim, and screw runners to the walls. The shims are then removed, with

Three coats of Fabulon, a tough plastic finish, were used throughout; each coat was carefully steel-wooled before next coat was applied.

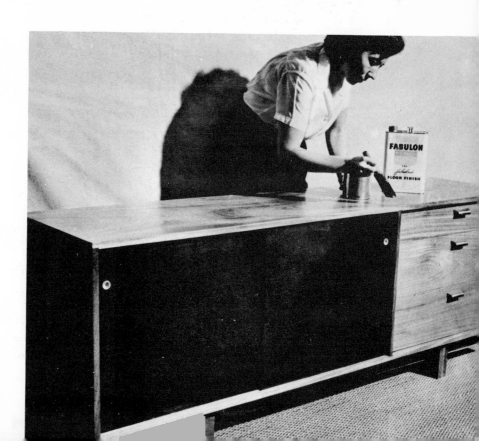

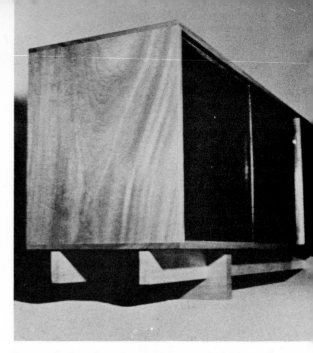

Unpretentious brass hardware (drawer pulls and finger cups) reflect basic simplicity of design.

Chest, over 6 ft. in length, seems to have "floating" quality because of unique base construction.

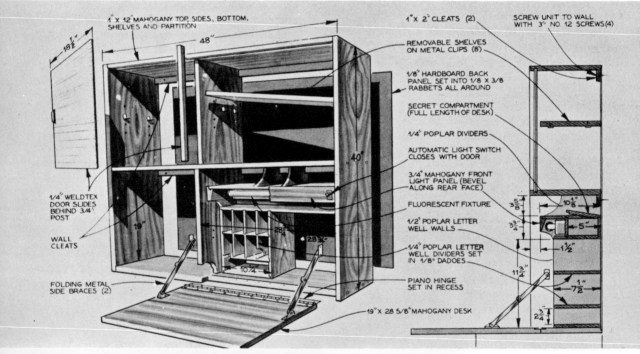

1" x 12" MAHOGANY TOP, SIDES, BOTTOM, SHELVES AND PARTITION

18 ½"

48"

1" x 2" CLEATS (2)

SCREW UNIT TO WALL WITH 3" NO 12 SCREWS (4)

REMOVABLE SHELVES ON METAL CLIPS (8)

1/8" HARDBOARD BACK PANEL SET INTO 1/8 x 3/8 RABBETS ALL AROUND

SECRET COMPARTMENT (FULL LENGTH OF DESK)

1/4" POPLAR DIVIDERS

AUTOMATIC LIGHT SWITCH CLOSES WITH DOOR

3/4" MAHOGANY FRONT LIGHT PANEL (BEVEL ALONG REAR FACE)

FLUORESCENT FIXTURE

1/2" POPLAR LETTER WELL WALLS

1/4" POPLAR LETTER WELL DIVIDERS SET IN 1/8" DADOES

PIANO HINGE SET IN RECESS

19" x 28 5/8" MAHOGANY DESK

40"

19"

28 ¾"

28 ¾"

10 ¼"

1/4" WELDTEX DOOR SLIDES BEHIND 3/4" POST

WALL CLEATS

FOLDING METAL SIDE BRACES (2)

3 5/8"
3/4"
11 3/4"
2 3/4"

10 1/8"
5"
1 ½"
1"
7 ½"

Secret compartments to delight any youngster can be cut into top of the fluorescent light housing of the wall desk.

The nine drawers of the completed chest offer a tremendous amount of easily accessible storage space. Two lower drawers on right-hand side are same height: top drawer is ideal for socks, hankies, etc.

the result that there remains exactly the right amount of play between drawers. Repeat this operation to find proper positions for all runners.

Sliding doors are made of ¼-in. hardboard. Shallow finger cups offer sufficient grip for opening and closing. Finish the unit as previously described. Screw the base to the cabinet, as shown in the diagram on page 293, and add drawer pulls to the three right-hand drawers.

Wall-Desk Unit: With his own desk to work on, you can be sure that getting Junior to do his homework will be less of a struggle for all concerned. Several unusual features have been incorporated in this design: a fluorescent fixture that lights up when the desk leaf is lowered, plenty of space for books and toys, and a letter compartment. Also, since all kids love to have a little secret hiding place, I built two small trapdoors over the light compartment.

Begin by cutting the sides, top, bottom, uprights, and shelf to size. Cut rabbets for the hardboard back, and the cutout along the right front of the bottom piece to accept the door, as well as a recess in this same member which will retain one leaf of a piano hinge. Make dadoes in the top and shelf to accept the ¼-in. Weldtex sliding door. You'll notice that the top upright is ripped as shown to permit the sliding door to function. The ¾-in. strip is added later as a visual effect. This upright is also notched at the top rear and dadoed under the shelf to accept wall cleats.

Assemble all of these elements with screws and glue. The fluorescent light

Pipe clamps hold desk's light housing in its proper position while it is being screwed in place.

Two screws are inserted on each side, and one through each side of the hidden compartments.

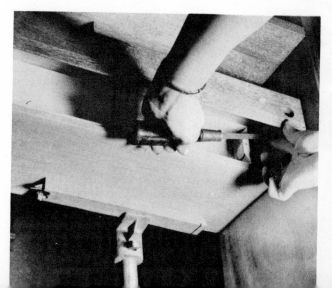

Vertical dividers for pigeonholes are forced into their dadoes from the back. No glue is required. Wall cleat may be seen under the top shelf.

After adding Masonite back, install desk leaf with piano hinge and pair of desk hinges. Leaf, when open, is partially supported by chest top.

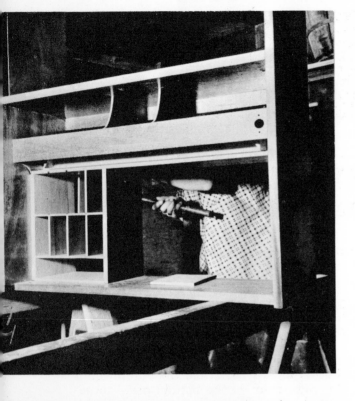

Small drawer under pigeonholes is constructed in similar fashion to the larger units in the chest. All the pulls are attached after finishing.

housing and pigeonhole unit is made of ¼ and ½-in. poplar, with the exception of the front of the former, which is ¾-in. mahogany, beveled as shown in the sketch on page 296.

The light housing is carefully assembled with the light box in place, then screwed into the cabinet from the sides while being retained with clamps. The pigeonhole unit is dadoed and nailed into place.

Vertical dividers are force-fitted from the back. The little drawer is glued and nailed together.

Note that the upper shelves in the cabinet are removable. Metal shelf supports, available at most hardware stores, are inserted into ⅜-in. deep holes. If you drill a series of parallel holes, you'll be able to shift the heights of the shelves to accommodate large books or albums.

Now cut the hardboard back, paint it any color you wish, and nail it into the rabbets already made. The unit is now ready for finishing.

Now the hinged door, which doubles as a desk surface, is cut to size and attached with one long piano hinge. Install the hinge brackets and a bullet catch, and remaining hardware.

The desk unit is not attached to the chest, but is screwed through the wall cleats into the studs with 3-in. screws. •

BILL OF MATERIALS

Note: All lumber, unless otherwise specified, is ¾-in. mahogany.

Radiator Cover

Top: 24 in. x 8 ft. (length variable)
Two right legs: 12x29½ in. (height variable)
Two left legs: 10¼x29½ in. (height variable)
Shelves: 10¼ in. x 12 ft.
Door: 15x39½ in.
Rear cleat and bottom framer: 1 in. x 2 in. x 12 ft.
Masonite back: 16½x40 in.
Bamboo slats for grille
Wastebasket: ½-in. stock or plywood sides, plastic or sheet metal back, ¼-in. dowels

Chest of Drawers

Top, bottom, sides, and two dividers: 19 in. x 21 ft.
Right-hand drawer fronts, bottom units (2): 8x57 in.
Top right-hand drawer front (1): 5½x28 in.
English-type drawer fronts (6): 5⅝ in. x 12 ft.
Backs and sides for 6 English-type drawers, ½-in. poplar: 6 in. x 30 ft.
Backs and sides for 2 top right-hand drawers, ½-in. poplar: 8 in. by 12 ft.

Back and sides for 1 top right-hand drawer, ½-in. poplar: 6 in. x 6 ft.
Drawer bottoms and back panel: 3 sheets of ⅛-in. x 4 ft. x 8 ft. Masonite
Splines for 3 right-hand drawers (6): ⅜ in. x ¾ in. x 10 ft. birch, oak, or maple
Splines for English-type drawers (12): ½ in. x 1½ in. x 24 ft. birch, oak, or maple
Splines for 2 bottom English-type drawers (4): ⅛ in. x ½ in. x 4 ft.
Sliding doors (2): ¼-in. tempered Masonite, 22x24 in.
Base: 1⅛ in. x 3¾ in. x 14 ft. birch stringers (2); base legs (2): 1¾ in. x 6 in. x 3 ft.
Hardware: finger cups, 3 drawer pulls

Wall Desk

Top, bottom, sides, and dividers: 12 in. x 24 ft.
Desk leaf: ⅝x19x28 in.
Wall cleats (2): 1 in. x 2 in. x 4 ft.
Light housing and pigeonhole unit: ¼ and ½-in. poplar
Light housing top (mahogany): ¾ in. x 2⅝ in. x 29 ft.
Top sliding door (1): ¼-in. Weldtex, 18½x20 in.
Masonite back: ⅛x40x48 in.
Hardware: automatic light switch; fluorescent light fixture; two drawer pulls; 1 piano hinge 28 in. long; pair of desk hinges; metal shelf supports (8)

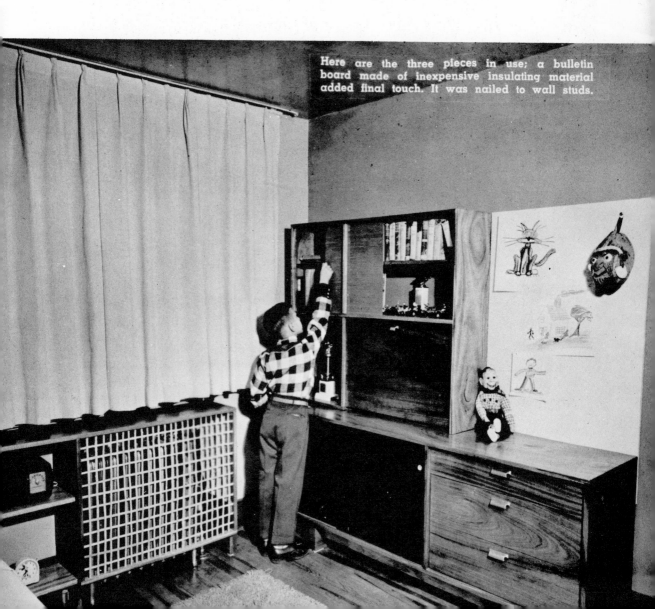

Here are the three pieces in use; a bulletin board made of inexpensive insulating material added final touch. It was nailed to wall studs.

Bells, Buzzers and Chimes

These useful household signals never need extensive repairs

THE ELECTRICAL wiring in a residence usually can be divided into (1) lighting and power systems and (2) those which are technically called signalling systems. The signalling systems comprise doorbells, doorchimes, call bells and buzzers, intercoms and fire and burglar alarms. All of these devices produce some sort of audible or visual signal.

Any person who hesitates to make repairs to the 120-volt light and power system because of the possibility of electric shock can install or repair home signalling systems without that anxiety or risk. These systems usually employ low voltage (6 to 24 volts) and are always safe to work on.

Simple Bell Circuit

The basic electric bell circuit consists of:
1. An electric bell; 2. a source of power; 3.

three pieces of wire; 4. a special switch called a push button.

The simplest source of power is a dry battery. A push button is actually a spring-loaded switch in which the contacts are closed only while the button is pressed. When the pressure is released the spring opens the contacts. Unless the button is pressed, the electrical circuit in which it is included is open and the bell cannot operate. When the switch is closed by pressing the button, current can flow and operate the bell. All bell, chime, buzzer and alarm signal systems utilize this fundamental circuit. A system may include several bells, buzzers, push buttons or chimes, etc., but the basic principle is always the same.

The mechanism of an electric bell is mounted on a metal base and is enclosed as protection against dust and mechanical damage. The "works" can be exposed for inspection or adjustment by removing the cover. When a low voltage (1½ to 6 volts) is applied to the terminal screws of the common electric bell, the round metal gong is tapped continuously by a small metal hammer or tapper until the current supply is discontinued. (There is also a "single-stroke" bell which rings once only each time the button is pressed. This type is used principally for coded signals.) The hammer which strikes the gong is attached to one end of an iron armature. The other end of the armature is supported on a spring-loaded pivot. The armature and its hammer vibrate back and forth through the

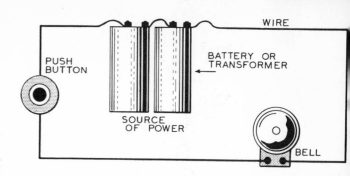

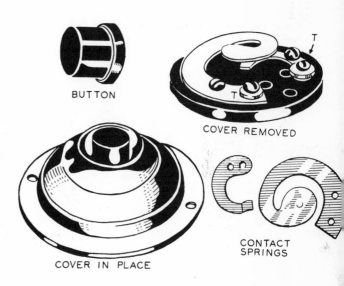

The details of construction of a common type of push button are shown in the illustration above.

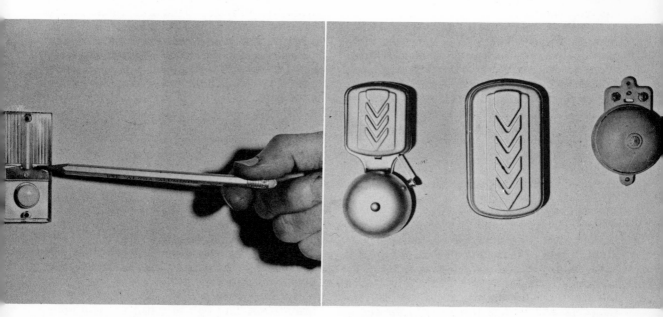

Pencil points to space for a name plate or card insertion on an illuminated push button fixture.

Common door bells. The gong on the center bell is enclosed. The bell at right is a monitor bell.

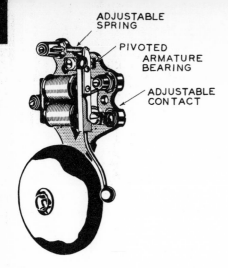

ADJUSTABLE SPRING

PIVOTED ARMATURE BEARING

ADJUSTABLE CONTACT

Pivot bell gives much louder signal than door-bell, is used for alarms where noise is needed.

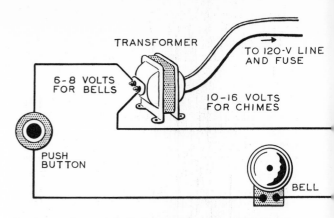

TRANSFORMER

TO 120-V LINE AND FUSE

6-8 VOLTS FOR BELLS

10-16 VOLTS FOR CHIMES

PUSH BUTTON

BELL

Drawing shows a bell circuit using the 120-volt AC stepped down by transformer as power source.

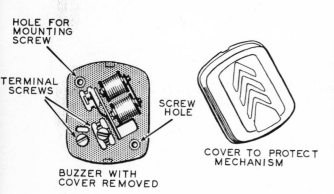

HOLE FOR MOUNTING SCREW

TERMINAL SCREWS

SCREW HOLE

COVER TO PROTECT MECHANISM

BUZZER WITH COVER REMOVED

The common call buzzer shown above has the same mechanism as a bell, but does not have a gong.

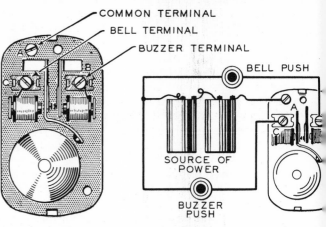

COMMON TERMINAL

BELL TERMINAL

BUZZER TERMINAL

BELL PUSH

SOURCE OF POWER

BUZZER PUSH

The wiring circuit for a combination bell-buzzer is a little more complicated, uses two dry cells.

action of the spring and the two electromagnets. Low-cost bells have only one electromagnet.

An electromagnet is a coil of wire wound around an iron core. The core becomes magnetized and attracts the armature when an electric current flows through the coil. As soon as the current ceases to flow, the core ceases to be a magnet and no longer attracts the armature. The bell armature is pulled away from the electromagnets by the spring-loaded pivot. When the armature is drawn toward the electromagnets, it not only swings the tapper or hammer against the gong but it also separates two contact points which are part of the bell circuit. The contact points are sometimes called the interrupter. When the contacts separate they open the circuit and interrupt the flow of current. The magnetic pull of the electromagnets then ceases. The spring action of the pivot then pulls the armature away from the electromagnets and brings the interrupter contacts together. The current flows again, the armature reverses its movement, the

tapper strikes the gong and the contacts open. This cycle is repeated rapidly as the armature vibrates back and forth in this manner and rings the gong as long as the push button is pressed.

Common electric door bells are the iron-box bell and the dome-shaped or monitor bell. The loud bells used in schools and public buildings for signals and alarms are similar to the iron-box bell in principle but are much larger and more powerful; pivot bells operate on 6 to 12 volts.

Buzzers have a mechanism similar to that of a bell but are not equipped with a gong and a tapper. The armature produces a buzzing sound when it vibrates but the sound is not as loud as that of a bell. In small houses it is customary to provide a bell or chime for a front door signal and a buzzer for the back door. A small buzzer is often used in offices to signal to a secretary, an office boy, a nurse, etc.

A combination bell-buzzer has two armatures. The bell armature taps a gong; the buzzer armature produces a buzzing sound. There are three terminals. One is

At the left is a combination bell-buzzer and in the center is a simple buzzer. The small buzzer at the right is called a Lungen buzzer. It is used where a loud buzz would be objectionable, has soft tone.

common to both the bell and buzzer. The same battery or source of power is shared. An illustration shows how this combination device is connected in circuit.

Batteries For Signalling Circuits

When a battery is required for a signalling circuit, No. 6 dry cells, measuring 6½ x 2⅝ inches, are generally used. Each cell delivers 1.5 volts when new. A single cell will ring an ordinary doorbell or buzzer provided the total length of wire in the circuit is not more than about 25 feet and the wire is not smaller than No. 18 B.S. Two cells are required for circuits containing 25 to 50 feet of wire and three, four or more cells for longer circuits. A rough rule to follow is: One cell for each 25 feet of wire in the circuit. Large bells of the pivot-bell type require two to four cells on a 25-foot circuit. The number of cells required for long circuits can be determined experimentally by starting with two or three cells and adding one cell at a time until the performance is satisfactory.

The cells in a battery for signalling circuits should be connected in series; that is, the short wire which runs from one cell to another should run from the positive (center terminal) to the negative (side terminal) of the next cell. Do *not* connect a negative terminal to a negative terminal or a positive terminal to a positive terminal. The bare ends of the wire should be scraped bright and the knurled nuts on the terminals of the dry cells tightened with a pair of pliers when the wires are in place.

Excess heat will shorten the life of dry cells. Although they are called dry, the cells contain a moist paste. A battery in a hot place will become dried out and inactive. Do not locate a dry cell battery where the temperature rises or falls above or below ordinary room temperature. The basement is usually a good location. Low temperatures slow the chemical action of dry cells and reduce their current output. Binding a battery of cells tightly together with cord or insulating tape will help in preventing loose connections.

Tighten the battery connections with a pair of pliers. Tie cells in a group using a string or some electrical tape.

The four dry cell batteries pictured at the right are correctly connected in series. You must always connect the positive to negative terminal.

A circuit for connecting two bells and one buzzer to a common power source (batteries, in this case) is illustrated at right.

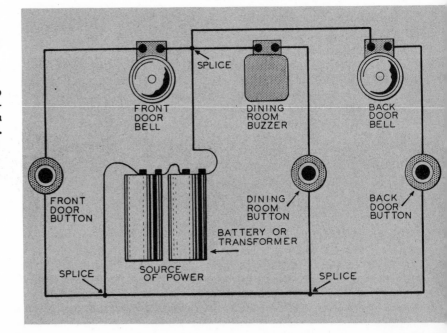

Bell-Ringing Transformers

In most houses built during the past two or three decades, a small step-down transformer replaces dry cells as a source of power for the doorbell system. Commonly called a "bell-ringer," this device reduces the 120-volt AC to 6 to 16 volts. The primary of the transformer is permanently connected to the 120-volt AC line, but draws so little current, except when a bell, buzzer or chime is sounded, that it barely overcomes the friction in the watt-hour meter. The increase in the monthly electric bill is so small that the annual cost of operating a bell-ringer is much less than the cost of replacing dry cells.

A bell-ringing transformer consists of two coils of wire wound on a sheet steel core and enclosed in a protective metal case. The primary terminals are usually two flexible wires, one white and one black. The white wire is connected to the grounded wire of a branch lighting circuit and the black wire to the live wire (black) of the same circuit. Some bell-ringers are designed to attach to a cover adapter which can be fastened to a standard outlet box in a lighting circuit to which the primary terminals can be connected. The connections are made and concealed behind the box cover.

A fused box in which a bell transformer can be mounted is on the market. The fuse is of no value unless the primary winding of the transformer should break down and form a short circuit. If this should occur,

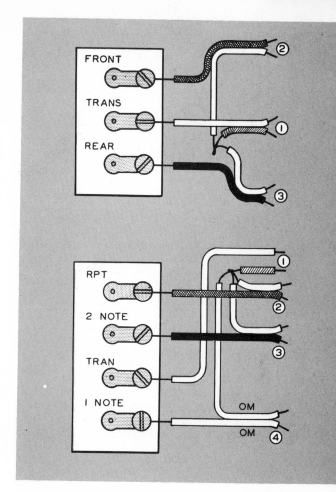

Terminal boards for two types of chimes. 1) connect to transformer. 2) connect to front door push button. 3) connect to rear door push button. 4) connect to side door push button. If there is no side door push button, omit wires marked OM in drawing.

Step-down transformer, called bell-ringing transformer, used as signalling circuit power source.

In many modern homes today a door chime will replace the old-fashioned harsh-sounding door bell.

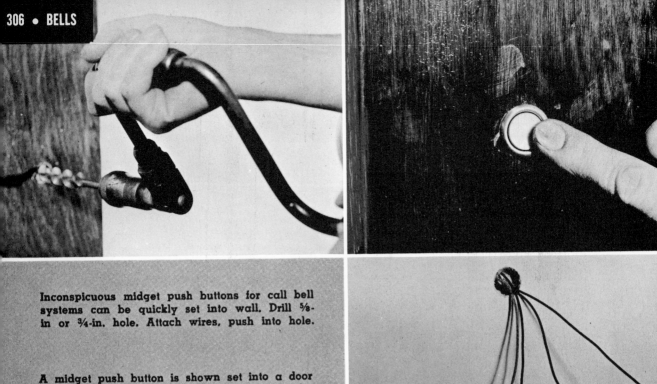

Inconspicuous midget push buttons for call bell systems can be quickly set into wall. Drill ⅝-in or ¾-in. hole. Attach wires, push into hole.

A midget push button is shown set into a door frame. A button of this type should always be mounted in woodwork and not in a plaster wall.

From four to six wires (depending on number of push buttons in circuit) must be led to a small hole in the wall back of a chime and connected.

the fuse in the branch circuit would be blown out and thus protect the circuit. The smallest plug type fuse is the 10 ampere size. Not enough current flows in either the primary or secondary to blow a 10 amp fuse. The current in the secondary is usually not more than 2 amperes even when short circuited. If dependable fuse protection for a bell-ringer is desired, it can be obtained only by using the "little fuses" illustrated on another page.

The secondary or low voltage terminals of the bell transformer may be provided with two knurled nuts or two flathead screws for connecting and clamping the wires. The secondary terminals are connected in a bell, buzzer or chime circuit in the same manner as if they were the terminals of a battery.

Door Chimes

This sound-producing device replaces the harsh ring of a gong with warm musical tones. There are two types. One has from one to four brass tubes suspended from a metal or plastic box designed to fasten to a wall. The other consists of two steel bars enclosed in a small wall-mounted cabinet. The musical tone is produced when a tube or a steel bar is struck by a small plunger operated by an electromagnet. If a chime has two or more musical tones, they may sound simultaneously or in succession depending upon the circuit arrangement. Usually the chime is connected so that two musical tones are produced when the push button at the front door is pressed and a single tone is sounded when a button at a rear or side door is pressed. Some small chimes will operate on a 4- to 6-volt battery or a 6- to 8-volt bell transformer, but most types require a step-down transformer with a secondary voltage of 10 to 24 volts.

Push Buttons

All push buttons are essentially switches which are held in the open position by a spring. The surface type push button consists of two spring contacts within a metal or plastic case. The contacts are normally held apart by the tension of the upper spring. Pressing an insulating button overcomes the tension and brings the two con-

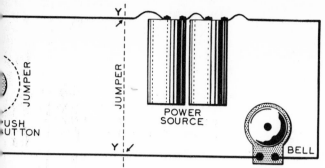

The way to trouble shoot a bell circuit using a jumper wire. This procedure is explained in text.

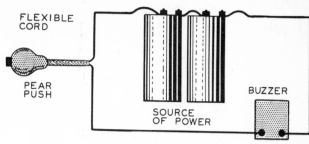

A sick-call buzzer circuit with pendant or pear push button, used in hospitals and nursing homes.

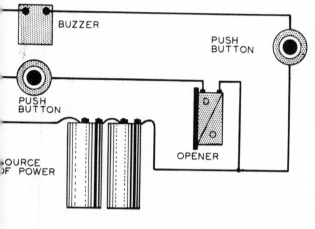

A circuit for a front door buzzer and a door opener using a common power source is shown above.

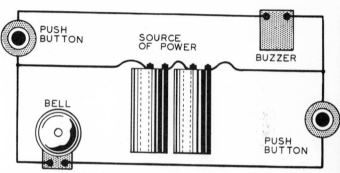

Circuit for return call system using a bell and buzzer. Transformer or batteries can be used.

tacts together, thus closing the circuit of the signalling system. The spring contacts and their terminals are mounted on an insulating base. Connections are made through the back of the push button and become concealed when the latter is mounted.

Midget push buttons, also called flush-mounted push buttons, which are smaller in size than the surface type, are convenient for use in wood trim, panelled walls, etc. They are mounted in place by drilling a hole in the mounting surface of the right size to provide a snug secure fit when the push button is forced into the hole.

First Aid For Bells, Buzzers, Chimes

When a push button is pressed and the bell, buzzer or chime which it controls fails to sound, look first for an open circuit and check the power supply.

An open circuit may be due to broken wire or loose or corroded connections. The vibration of a bell or buzzer armature sometimes loosens the terminal screws. Loose connections at terminals may be avoided by using small lock washers on all terminals including those on the battery or transformer. Dirt on the contact points of a bell or buzzer can cause an open circuit. To remedy this, wipe the contact surfaces with a strip of No. 000 sandpaper, followed by a strip of clean paper or cloth to remove all dust and abrasive.

The atmosphere also corrodes the contacts on a push button. They should be inspected often and cleaned if necessary. If the terminals on a push button are short circuited with a screwdriver or knife blade and the bell rings but does not ring when the button is pressed, the push button should be replaced.

Dry cells usually give good service for a year or even two years, under ordinary conditions, in a doorbell circuit. They may not last more than a few months if subjected to hard use. A dry cell in good condition should indicate 1.5 volts on a voltmeter and 25 amperes when connected to an ammeter *for a second or two.* A No. 6 dry cell which indicates only 10 amperes or less should be replaced. Test instruments are not always available to the

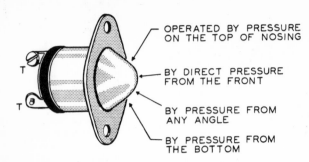

OPERATED BY PRESSURE ON THE TOP OF NOSING

BY DIRECT PRESSURE FROM THE FRONT

BY PRESSURE FROM ANY ANGLE

BY PRESSURE FROM THE BOTTOM

The contact for a simple burglar system. It is set in a door frame or a window frame. It closes an ordinary bell circuit when window or door is opened.

handy man, but he can use a "rough and ready" method of checking. Disconnect the cells in the battery and connect one to the bell, using two short pieces of No. 18 wire not over two feet long to make the connection. If the bell is in good working order and the dry cell is O.K., the bell will ring vigorously. If the bell rings feebly or not at all, it is advisable to replace the cell with a new one. Test each battery in this manner.

Bell-ringing transformers seldom burn out or break down. When a transformer supplies the power for a signalling circuit, an apparent power failure may be due to a broken wire, loose or dirty connections or a blown fuse. A transformer with a secondary voltage of 6 to 8 volts is in good condition if it will light a 6-volt lamp (small auto lamp) connected to the secondary terminals.

Another method of testing a transformer is to rub a screwdriver blade across the secondary terminals. If this produces small sparks, the transformer is operating.

A transformer connected to the 120-volt power supply may feel slightly warm. This is normal. On the other hand, a transformer which is hot to the touch is either overloaded or short circuited. A transformer which shows discoloration apparently due to heat may be burned out.

Chime circuits are subject to the same troubles as bell and buzzer circuits. There may be a power failure, a broken wire, loose connections, dirty contacts on the push button, etc. Since chimes do not have vibrating contacts, maintenance of the chime mechanism is usually limited to cleaning out dust and dirt and tightening connections. The electromagnets in a chime are of the solenoid type. The wire is wound on a spool having a hollow sleeve in the center. The iron core in a solenoid is called a "plunger." The plunger is not fixed in the winding like the iron core of an electromagnet, but can move back and forth in the sleeve. When current flows

through the solenoid, magnetism pulls the plunger into the coil. When the current ceases, the magnetism disappears and a spring pushes the plunger back and partly out of the coil. When the plunger is pulled into the coil it strikes one of the bars or tubes. The blow produces a musical tone like that of a xylophone. To clean the plunger or "striker" and sleeve, use lighter fluid or naphtha. Under no circumstances use any oil on these parts. Oil, in time, will thicken, becoming gummy and cause the striker to stick.

Open Circuit Trouble Shooting

An unintentional open circuit is probably the most common trouble in signalling systems. Trouble shooting should begin with a careful examination of each piece of equipment. If this does not reveal the fault the "jumper," or test wire, method of looking for the open circuit should be used. This is illustrated in one of the bell circuit diagrams. Scrape the insulation off the circuit wires for about ¼ inch at the points indicated in the diagram by XX and YY. Connect the two bare spots at X and X with a short piece of No. 18 wire, called a "jumper," as indicated by the dotted line in the diagram. If the bell, buzzer or chime does not signal when the push button is pressed but responds when the jumper is connected to X and X, the push button (or its connections) is faulty.

If a jumper wire connected to points X and X does not produce a signal, connect a second jumper at the points indicated by Y and Y. If the bell, buzzer or chime gives a signal when this connection is made, the test indicates a weak battery, a break in the wiring, or a poor connection somewhere in the wires leading to the push button which are to the left of Y and Y in the circuit diagram.

Call Systems

Illness comes to almost every home at one time or another. A permanent or even

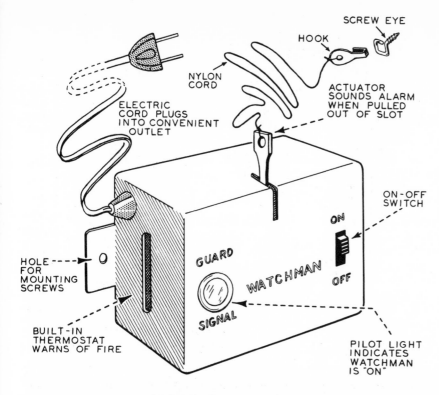

SCREW EYE

HOOK

NYLON CORD

ACTUATOR SOUNDS ALARM WHEN PULLED OUT OF SLOT

ELECTRIC CORD PLUGS INTO CONVENIENT OUTLET

ON-OFF SWITCH

ON

OFF

GUARD

WATCHMAN

SIGNAL

HOLE FOR MOUNTING SCREWS

BUILT-IN THERMOSTAT WARNS OF FIRE

PILOT LIGHT INDICATES WATCHMAN IS "ON"

"Watchman" serves both as a fire alarm and a burglar alarm when installed as described in text. Below is photograph of the installation on a window—the burglar only has to lift it an inch and the alarm rings.

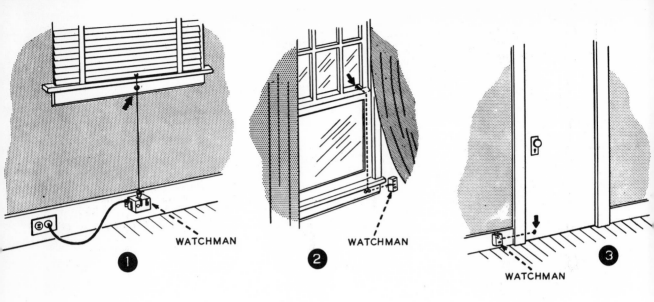

Three typical watchman installations. 1. The actuator cord is attached to the Venetian blind. 2. The actuator cord is attached to upper sash, protecting both sections. 3. Cord attached to door.

a temporary call buzzer will often save considerable running back and forth to attend the needs of an invalid or patient. A small buzzer, pear push button, two dry cells or a transformer and the necessary wiring can be installed quickly to perform this valuable service. The pear-shaped or pendant push button should be connected to a 6 to 10 foot length of flexible double conductor wire so that it can be hung on a bed post where the sick person can reach it.

It is sometimes of great convenience to have a signalling system whereby a button can be pressed to notify members of a household who are in a basement workshop, garage or third floor that they are wanted at the telephone, to come to dinner, etc. The system is more useful when it is a return call system so that the person who is signalled can also press a button to sound a buzzer which will indicate that the call has been heard and will be responded to.

Electric Door Openers

These are installed in the door frame of the main entrance to small apartment houses and are operated by push buttons in the apartments. The door opener replaces the common strike plate of a doorlock. When current flows through a pair of electromagnets in the door opener, they pull the strike plate on the opener out of the way so that a locked door can be pushed open from the outside without a key. A door opener circuit consists of a push but-

ton, door opener and source of power. A push button is located in the kitchen or foyer near the door bell or buzzer of each apartment. Pressing one of these buttons will release the door lock and make it unnecessary to go to the door to open it when the doorbell has been rung.

Wiring For Signal Systems

No. 18 B.S. gauge copper "annunciator" wire is commonly installed for indoor signalling systems. If the circuit is more than 75 feet long it is advisable to use No. 16. Annunciator wire is insulated with two layers of wax impregnated cotton yarn or a layer of plastic, depending upon the manufacturer. The wire is usually fastened in place with staples. Since insulation on the annunciator wire is easily damaged the staples should be the insulated type and two wires should not be placed under the same staple. Do not drive the staples too hard or they may cut through the insulation on the wire and sometimes through the wire itself. When possible the wiring should be concealed, not only for the sake of appearance but also to protect it from damage.

Electric Watchmen Stand Guard

A protective burglar alarm system for the average home can be installed by the amateur electrician at small cost. A push-button device called a contactor is installed in each window and door frame it is desired to protect. When such a window or door is opened, a contact is made with-

The thermostat which operates the fire alarm system is only 1½ inches in diameter, and is inconspicuous.

in the contactor and an alarm set off. Contactors may be installed in the hinge side, latch side or top of door frames, in the side of window frames, at the sides, top or bottom of transoms. The contactor operates by pressure from top, bottom, front or from any angle. The contactors are connected in parallel and made part of a circuit which includes a switch, 6-inch alarm bell and a source of electric current. The system may be operated on current supplied by No. 6 dry cells or by a bell-ringer transformer connected to a 120-volt power source.

If a transformer is used, failure of the 120-volt power supply will make the alarm system inoperative. An intruder who may know of the existence of the protective system can render it inoperative by cutting the service wire. No. 6 dry cells will last about a year before needing replacement and are a source of power which cannot be tampered with from outside the premises.

A stairway can be used to detect the presence of an intruder by installing an electric mat. It operates in the same manner as a push button. Pressure on the mat will close an electric contact and operate the alarm. The matting can be placed on a step on a staircase or where a person would be most likely to step on it. It is equally effective when placed under a rug or other floor covering.

A switch is placed in the circuit so that the system can be made inoperative during the daytime when windows and doors would normally be opened and closed by

persons dwelling in the house. However, an alarm which would sound every time a window or door is opened would be a nuisance. Those with the right of entry must be able to enter while the system is in operation or it must be turned off during the daytime. An ordinary switch can be opened or closed by an unauthorized person. To solve this problem, a lock switch is available which can be used to turn the entire alarm system on or off by means of an ordinary key.

One of the illustrations shows a combination burglar and fire alarm called a "Watchman" which can be installed in half an hour. It depends upon string-tripping for operation as a burglar alarm. A black nylon thread connected to the watchman is fastened to doors and windows or stretched across a passageway. Any pressure on the thread, such as would result from opening a window or door or when an intruder's leg came into contact with it, would close a contact and set off the alarm.

The Watchman is a small steel cabinet containing a thermostat, alarm bell, pilot light, "actuator," on-off switch and a small step-down transformer. The cabinet is designed to be fastened to the baseboard under a window or in another suitable spot. An electric cord plugs into a convenient outlet to power the Watchman. The actuator is a strip of plastic or fiber which slips into a slot in the cabinet and separates two contact points. One or more strong nylon cords are tied to the actuator and fastened to a door, window frame, etc. Any disturbance of the cord will pull the actuator from between the contact points and the latter will close and set off the alarm. The on-off switch enables you to render the alarm operative when protection is desired or to turn it off when house cleaning is being done and the alarm might be accidentally disturbed. The pilot light is a visible signal showing that the unit is on.

A number of windows or doors in the same room can be connected to one Watchman. Use a screw eye in each window frame. Protect casement windows by using two cords attached to the actuator at one end and to two wire hooks at the other end. Fasten the hooks to the window handles and if the window is opened the alarm will ring.

The thermostat in the cabinet will close two contacts and ring the alarm bell if the room temperature rises to about 140 degrees F, so in one of these devices you have both a fire and a burglar alarm.

Home Fire Alarm System

Minutes, even seconds count when a home or building catches fire, precious minutes in which you and others can leave

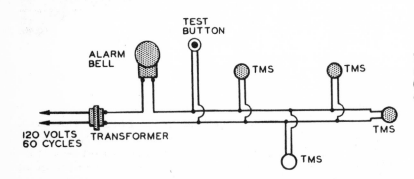

The circuit diagram for fire alarm system utilizing three thermostats (TMS). Additional thermostats can easily be incorporated if needed.

To insure maximum protection for your home and family, the bell in your fire alarm system should be a loud-ringing six-inch bell like the one shown here at the left, compared with a common doorbell.

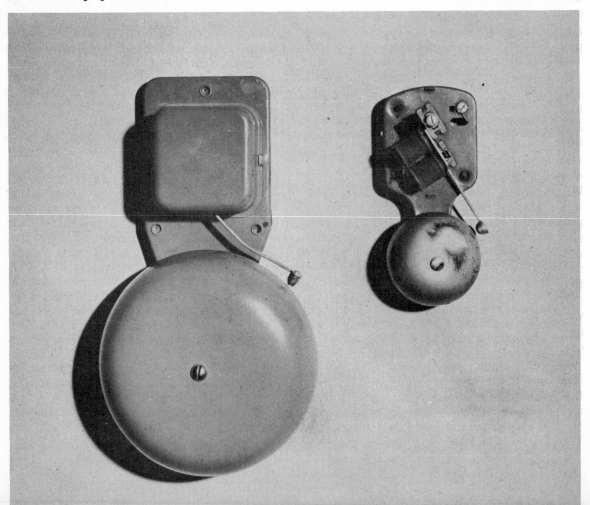

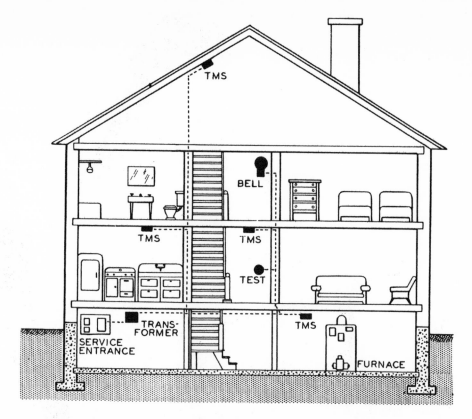

The cross section sketch of a small house shows the principal locations for fire alarm thermostats (TMS). The test button (TEST) is located in a hallway to make it convenient for nightly testing.

the premises in safety and summon aid. A blaze which is discovered soon enough can often be put out with a bucket of water or a small extinguisher. A short time later the efforts of two fire companies might not quench it.

Small, inconspicuous, plastic-enclosed thermostats which operate at 140 degrees F make it possible to install an inexpensive automatic fire alarm system. You can make the installation yourself. The thermostats are heat-operated switches. The contacts remain open until the surrounding air reaches a temperature of 140 degrees F, then they close the circuit and the alarm bell rings.

An electric bell with a 6-inch gong should be installed to sound the alarm. Current for the circuit can be supplied by a 120-volt transformer with an 8 to 10-volt secondary or by a 6 to 9-volt dry cell battery. Since fires are due sometimes to defective wiring, a fuse may blow and render the alarm system inoperative when it is connected to the AC lighting system. No. 6 dry cells will give service for a year or more if they are not located near a furnace or other excessively warm place where they are subjected to more than

normal room temperatures. A push button can be connected in the circuit in parallel with one of the thermostats and used as a "test button." If all connections are tight and the dry cells are in good condition, the alarm will ring.

The alarm bell should be located in a hall where its sound can be heard throughout the house. The thermostats should be mounted on the wall near the ceiling. The hot air from even a small blaze will rise to the ceiling and operate the thermostat much sooner than when the thermostat is located lower down. One thermostat should be located in the kitchen, one in the basement or cellar and one in the attic near the peak of the roof. Others can be installed wherever they may be deemed necessary.

Ordinary bell wire should be used to form the circuit. This can be installed along molding or concealed in the walls as electric light wiring. If there are more than 150 feet of wire in that part of the circuit which includes the alarm bell, power supply and most remote thermostat, it may be necessary to increase the power supply voltage in order to make the bell sound loud and clear. •

The sturdy unit has room for books, pencils and papers in the deep storage shelf underneath the desk top.

play-school bench

Craftsmen of Central Europe created this design for their children years ago. Its classic lines and plentiful storage space meet modern needs, too.

Photos by Mike Bonvino

Place both side panels with front edges together, and mark off shelf, front panel, bottom support.

Mount front panel (F) to shelf (E), holding (F) flush on bottom with (G) and ends as illustrated.

Mount panel and shelf assembly between both side panels (D), holding top edges of all parts flush.

Rout pencil troughs ¼ inch wide by 3/16 inch deep, 2 inches apart and 2 inches in from edge.

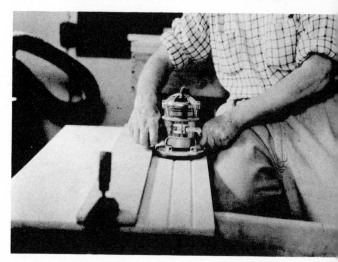

THIS BENCH is actually an old-timer, having been used years ago in Central Europe to inspire children to do their play-drawing, sketching, and their homework during the lower grade-school years.

The ample storage shelf teaches your child to keep things in place, and also relieves mother from having to do too much picking up.

The model was built from ¾-inch birch Weldwood plywood with matching solid wood for cleats. Then it was finished off with Keystone Seat and Pew Varnish.

After cutting out all pieces as shown in the plywood layout chart, mark them for identification. Temporarily tack together the side panels (D) and the seat supports (C), keeping the edges flush. Sand all edges smooth and plane the top and bottom edges straight. Take the pieces apart; mark guide lines for the shelf assembly.

Note that there is also a bottom support (not shown in the drawing), ¾x6x33 inches, mounted between both side panels (D), flush with the bottom edge and 3 inches from the front edges of (D).

On the outside of panels (D), bore four ½-inch holes 5⁄16 inch deep, then 3⁄16-inch holes all the way through, for front panel (F); also three holes for the bottom support. On the top (A), bore three similar holes 1⅛ inches from each side edge, starting the first hole 1⅜ inches from the front and the last hole 5 inches from the

Turn assembly upside down on desk top and mark guide lines on bottom surface to insure accuracy.

All edges of shelf assembly must be planed flush so that working surface (A) can be mounted evenly.

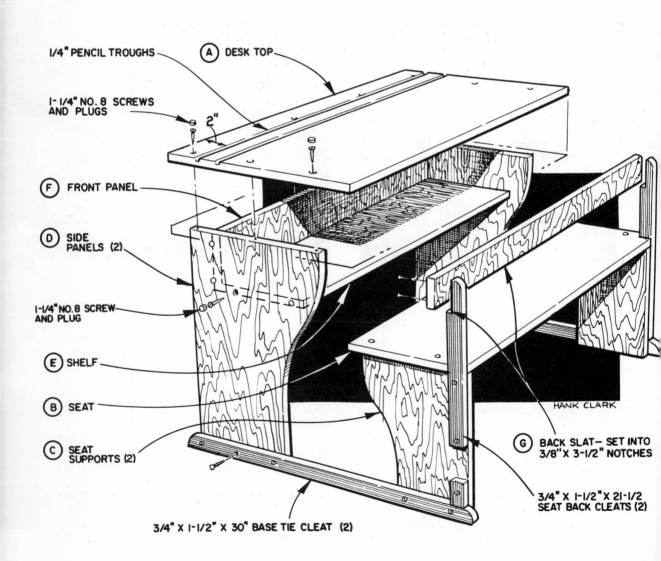

1/4" PENCIL TROUGHS

(A) DESK TOP

1-1/4" NO. 8 SCREWS AND PLUGS

2"

(F) FRONT PANEL

(D) SIDE PANELS (2)

1-1/4" NO.8 SCREW AND PLUG

(E) SHELF

(B) SEAT

(C) SEAT SUPPORTS (2)

HANK CLARK

(G) BACK SLAT— SET INTO 3/8" X 3-1/2" NOTCHES

3/4" X 1-1/2" X 21-1/2 SEAT BACK CLEATS (2)

3/4" X 1-1/2" X 30" BASE TIE CLEAT (2)

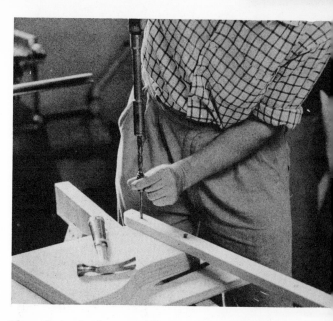

After boring all holes, mount top with glue and 1¼-inch No. 8 flathead screws. Make edges flush.

Mount base tie cleats outside seat supports flush on bottom, with glue, 1¼-inch No. 12 flathead screws.

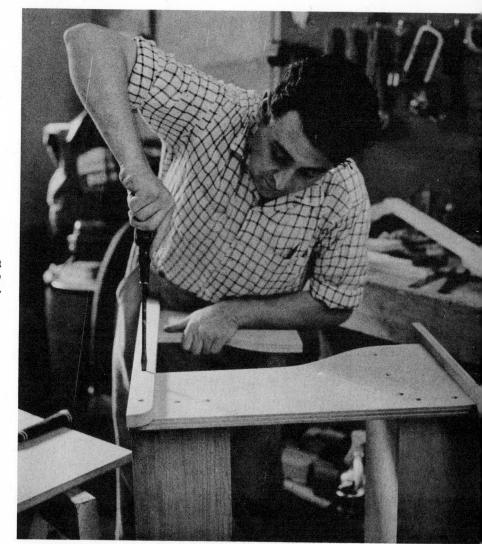

Mount base tie cleat-seat support assemblies to side panels, cleats extending.

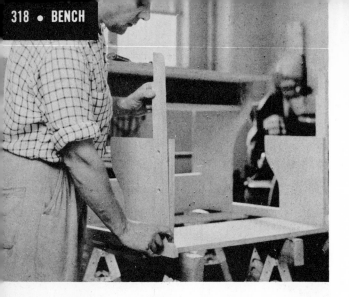

Mount seat and back cleats to seat supports flush in back and snug against both the base tie cleats.

With seat temporarily in place, mark for ¾ x 1½-inch notch with try square. Cut with hand saw.

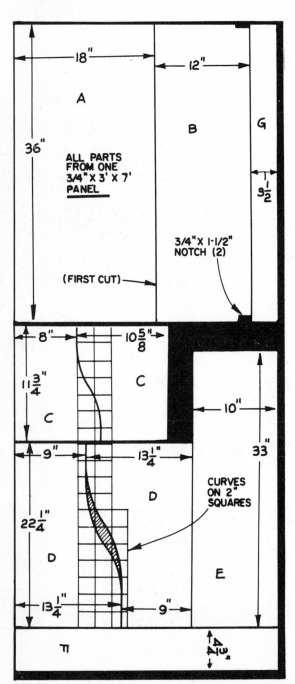

back; also bore two holes 2⅛ inches from the front and 13 inches from each end.

In the front panel (F), ⅜ inch from the bottom edge, bore five equally spaced ½-inch holes ⁵⁄₁₆ inch deep, then ³⁄₁₆-inch holes all the way through; start ¾ inch from each end. Next, temporarily tack together two ¾x1½x30-inch matching solid wood strips and round the ends to a 1⅜-inch radius, quarter-round; drill ¼-inch countersunk holes, at 2¼, 6, and 9¾ inches from one end, at 2¼ and 8¾ inches from the other end.

Round off the top end of two tacked-together seat back cleats and notch out for back slat (G). Bore ¼-inch holes, countersunk, at ¾, 5⅞, and 11 inches from the bottom.

On seat (B), 1⅛ inches from the sides, bore three holes similar to those in (A); locate the end holes 2⅛ inches from the front and back.

On back slat (G) bore two holes ⅜ inch from each end as done previously, starting ¾inch from the top and bottom edges.

MATERIAL LIST

¾" birch Weldwood plywood (for all parts except cleats), 3 x 7 ft.
1" matching solid wood (cleats, long-grain plugs), 4" x 5 ft.
4 dz. flathead screws, 1¼" No. 8
16 flathead screws, 1¼" No. 12
Presto-Set white liquid glue
Matching putty
Sandpaper (preferably garnet paper), Nos. ½, 2/0, 4/0.

Mount back slat with glue and 1¼ No. 8 flathead screws, holding seat flush with seat back cleats.

Assemble the desk, using glue and 1¼-inch No. 8 flathead screws. First mount front panel (F) to shelf (E), holding (F) flush on the bottom with (E) and ends. Fill the holes with matching ½-inch long-grain plugs (see page 9).

Mount the shelf assembly between both panels (D), lining up with the guide lines, and then mount top (A). Before mounting (A), all edges of the desk assembly must be flush.

Attach all cleats, with glue and 1¼-inch No. 12 flathead screws. Mount the base tie cleats to seat supports (C), keeping them flush on the bottom and leaving 1½ inches extending in back. Then fasten seat supports (C) to sides (D), leaving the base tie cleats extending. Mount the seat back cleats flush with the back edge of (C) and snug against the base tie cleat.

Put seat (B) in place, and mark it for notches in both back corners. Mount the seat with glue and 1¼-inch No. 8 flathead screws. Mount the long back slat.

Make pencil troughs, using a guide strip with a portable router. If by hand, use a back saw against a guide strip with a ¼-inch chisel and ground plane. ●

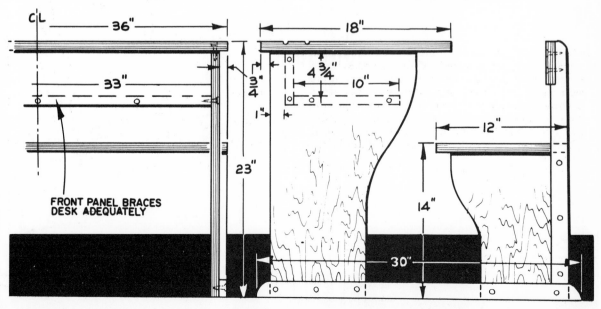

FRONT PANEL BRACES DESK ADEQUATELY

MAKE THIS combination bench and railing any
length you need for seating space plus protection
from falling over an elevation. The bench needs
only one standard about every four or five feet.

STANDARDS are made to dimensions shown, using 5/4 stock, oak or sound redwood or pine. If you
have trouble finding oak, ask lumber dealer for
stair treads which cut efficiently into these sizes.
Speediest assembly of standards comes with ordinary lapped joints, held with plastic resin glue
and two 2-inch No. 10 brass screws. For a neater
job—but not necessarily stronger—half-lap joints.

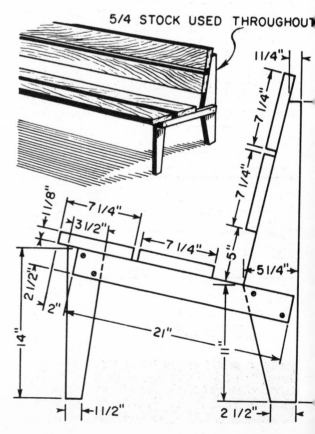

5/4 STOCK USED THROUGHOUT

Boundary Bench

This unit provides plenty of seating space and also forms an attractive terrace railing

THIS spacious, modern-design bench, stretching almost 16 feet along one side of a wooden deck and about 12 on the other, has two purposes. One is to provide a lot of seating. The other is to form a railing along the two sides of the deck which are, like the edges of many terraces and most decks, high enough to represent a hazard should someone accidentally step off. In normal use it is not occupied in the manner of wallflowers decorating the edges of a dance floor. Rather, a circular table goes in front of the angle for one grouping, and other tables are placed near the ends. Thus the bench forms the major seating for three different terrace groupings, in addition to its safety function.

It is very simple to build, comprising only seven identical standards to support seat and back (fewer, of course, if you should build the railing-bench shorter since one support is required about every 4 feet). The supports are made of 5/4 oak, the seats and backs are 5/4 redwood. Oak was used for extra strength; it would have been rugged enough if 5/4 redwood had been used. In finish, the redwood was double coated with Cedar Rez; the standards with dark turquoise enamel.

Simplicity Stressed

The drawing shows the standards are made as simply as possible with joints lapped instead of half-lapped, fastened with screws and Weldwood glue. There are only two construction tricks. One is placing the standards on their backs and attaching the boards for the back first. This

TAPERED BACK RESTS and front legs are easy to make in a hurry with taper jig (see right) which you set up after drawing outline on stock, as is shown here. Only one leg needs to be laid out.

WITH PRE-SET TAPER JIG locked in position, subsequent cuts can all be made with identical results provided "blanks" you cut from are uniform in width and length. Overlapping saves wood.

AFTER TAPERS are cut on all parts, set up for right-angle crosscutting and square all ends against faces as indicated in drawing. Clamping stop to saw insures all pieces being identical.

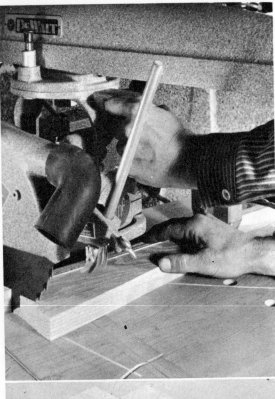

SAVE TIME and insure uniformity in all supports by assembling subsequent ones over the first. Use same unit for guide to all supports so you won't repeat and magnify any error that creeps in.

FAST WAY to prebore shank holes and pilot holes is to clamp pieces in position, then use "Screw Mates" in electric drill. Apply glue first; then when screws are driven, joint is speedily finished.

is simpler than attempting to install the seats first.

The other trick involves the fairly complicated job of joining the seats and backs together at the corner, since both of them are angled and require a compound miter. This was done by the simple expedient of cutting a simple 45-degree miter first, then positioning the two sections together snugly, after which a vertical saw cut was made *in* the joint. After that cut was made, the joint was closed up again and another cut made. Cutting from the top of the seat and the front of the back, no visible splintering resulted. To secure the joint, two 2-inch No. 8 brass screws went through

AFTER SUPPORTS are completed, before finishing, knock off corners with sandpaper to avoid sharp corner that won't hold finish well. Use any good outdoor enamel, three coats sanding between.

each plank into the end of the other plank.

Brass screws, by the way, were used entirely on this job. They were drawn flush without countersinking, and no attempt was made to fill or seal them. As you can see, the job was designed for simplicity.

Since the function as a railing requires immobility, the benches were fastened firmly in place at their positions along the two sides of the deck.

With these instructions, plus the drawings and photographs shown on these pages, you should have no trouble whatsoever in building this boundary bench. And you should be more than pleased with your final result. •

WOOD PRESERVATIVES

Wood deteriorates for two reasons: fungus and insects. Keep it dry and away from insects, and it will last longer than you do. But it's hard to keep outdoor furniture, terraces, posts, etc., dry. So, treat the wood with chemicals to prevent fungus, kill or repel insects.

The newest and most useful wood preservative for the homeowner is based on the chemical "pentachlorphenol." Most paint and building supply outlets sell preservatives containing "penta" and it always says so on the can. It comes in two forms:

One is ready-to-use, a mixture with mineral spirits which can be painted over. Use it when the good looks of natural wood are desired, since it does not discolor wood appreciably. Use it when subsequent painting or varnishing is in order.

The other is a stock solution to be mixed with about 10 parts of used crankcase oil, fuel oil or kerosene. It stains and cannot normally be painted over. Use it for the underground ends of posts and other places which do not show. It is more effective than the ready-to-use kind.

Penta formulas may also include a water repellent which makes them more effective.

Either way, penetration of the wood is important, the degree of penetration marking the degree of protection. Wood must be flooded with it. Two applications are essential. Endgrain is most subject to rot and should be soaked, usually possible by standing the ends of the stock in a container of preservative.

And—for maximum protection—use a preservative *plus* paint on *all* surfaces of the wood.

PRESERVATIVE is most needed where post is in contact with earth. Saturate end of post very well.

PAINT ROLLER applies preservative. Place wooden strips between boards so air dries it quickly.

Cobbler's Bench

A workbench of the past is adapted for use in the modern living room

THE RUGGED old cobbler's bench has come up in the world! Now it serves as a cocktail table to grace handsome living rooms. It is one of the more interesting examples of a strictly utilitarian item adapted for decorative purposes. Because of its sound proportions, its interesting contours and the association with long-ago days, the cobbler's bench is very popular among collectors of Early American replicas.

Whether of soft pine, dented and made to look blackened with age, or in smooth and gleaming maple, the cobbler's bench is still a conversation piece, particularly when made of very old wood, salvaged perhaps from an old barn or floor planks.

This coffee table combines sturdy basic construction with "light" frills on top such as the sliding cover planter section, the

"dished" ring at one end, and the useful little compartments. An ample drawer underneath will be found handy for entertainment accessories such as playing cards, chessmen, etc., or coasters and cigarettes.

When made of pine, the soft wood is easily fashioned to the various shapes. Joining is done with screws hidden with plug inserts cut from dowels. Maple is more difficult to work, requiring real sharp tools for careful jointing and gluing.

The first problem is to get a board of the right thickness and at least 15 inches wide for the bench top. The board should be a full one inch thick (referred to as 5/4 stock) rather than the usual ¾-inch board. This may be obtained in 8- or 10-inch width, so it will be necessary to glue up two pieces edge to edge. When gluing, place the boards together on a table with waxed

The informal cobbler's bench rivals the coffee table designs of other periods for popularity as furniture for living room.

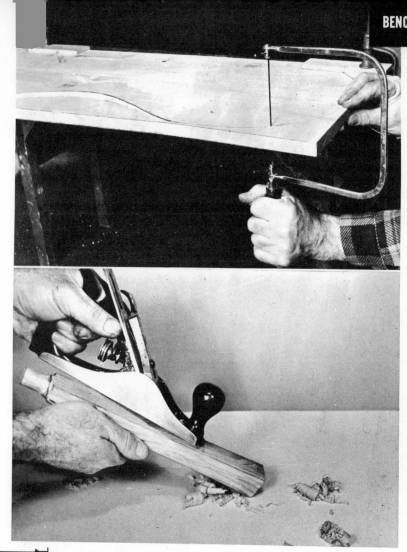

Top is cut in traditional shape with a coping saw. The glued boards are reenforced by two cleats attached from underneath.

After marking guide lines the four legs are "reverse tapered" on the outside only, to give them an appearance of outward slope.

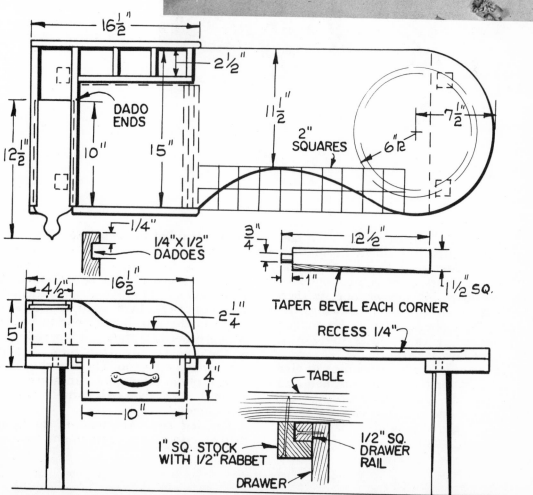

16½"

2½"

DADO ENDS

10"

15"

12½"

11½"

2" SQUARES

7½"

6" R

¼"

1/4"X 1/2" DADOES

¾"

12½"

1"

1½" SQ.

TAPER BEVEL EACH CORNER

RECESS 1/4"

4½"

16½"

2¼"

5"

4"

10"

TABLE

1" SQ. STOCK WITH 1/2"RABBET

DRAWER

1/2" SQ. DRAWER RAIL

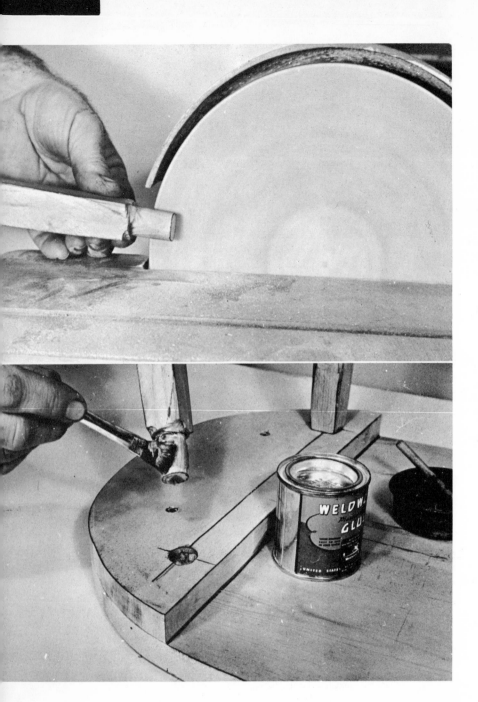

The leg ends are tenoned for a ¾-inch hole. Tenons can be whittled roughly and then rounded by turning against a disc sander.

Legs are glued into holes drilled two inches from the sides into the cleat. Make sure that auger does not pierce upper surface.

paper underneath, put clamps at each end to hold the center line down flush, then apply clamp pressure uniformly along the outside edges to bring the center together.

The top board, 40 inches long, is then shaped out as shown in the drawings. At this time, the dished ring may be gouged out, if desired, with a chisel to ¼-inch depth at the lowest part.

The ends are of double thickness to give better support for the leg tenons, and also to reinforce the glued up boards of the bench top. At one end, the cleat is 1- by 4-inch board; the other end is shaped from 1- by 8-inch stock to conform to the rounded end of the bench top. These cleats are fitted flush with the top along the outside edges, in keeping with the design.

The legs are of 1½- by 1½-inch stock, of the same kind of wood as the bench top. The legs are set in straight, that is, at right angle to the top, but appear to be sloped outward because they are tapered upward on the outside only. Thus they are slightly narrower at the top. The tapering is done with a plane after guide lines are marked along the leg edges. All corners of the legs are rounded.

The leg ends are tenoned to fit holes drilled into cleats. You might turn these

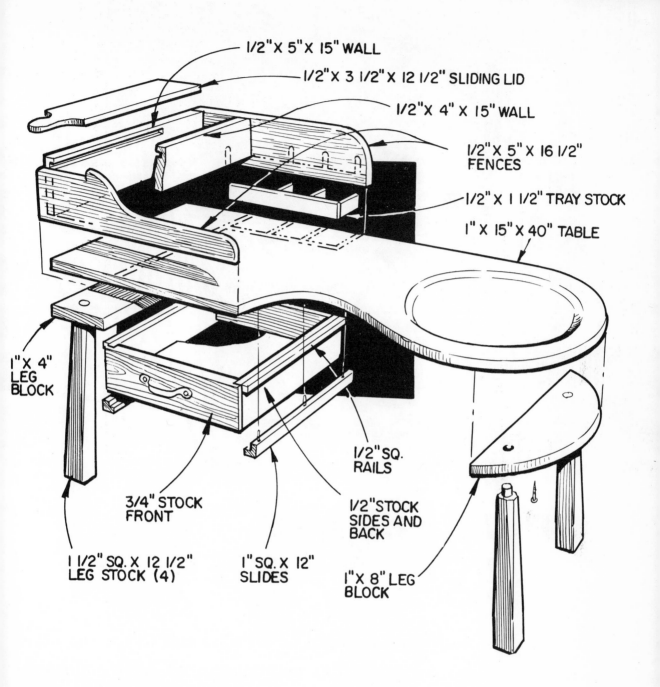

1/2" X 5" X 15" WALL

1/2" X 3 1/2" X 12 1/2" SLIDING LID

1/2" X 4" X 15" WALL

1/2" X 5" X 16 1/2" FENCES

1/2" X 1 1/2" TRAY STOCK

1" X 15" X 40" TABLE

1" X 4" LEG BLOCK

1/2" SQ. RAILS

3/4" STOCK FRONT

1/2" STOCK SIDES AND BACK

1 1/2" SQ. X 12 1/2" LEG STOCK (4)

1" SQ. X 12" SLIDES

1" X 8" LEG BLOCK

tenons on a lathe or whittle them to shape. An easier, but less effective way, is to drill for dowel inserts. To find the center, draw diagonal lines between the corners of the narrower end, drill ¾-inch holes about one inch deep and glue in dowels so that one inch extends for the tenon.

The leg holes are drilled straight into the cleats of the bench top, and the legs are glued in. A bit of adjustment with a wood rasp will be necessary to equalize the leg lengths so the table stands steady.

With this stage completed you have the basic cobbler's bench. The "superstructure" can be added at leisure: the compart-ment dividers, the planter recess, the rim molding, and the handy drawer slung un-derneath. Top edges of all partitions are neatly rounded. The drawer has a pair of side runners that fit into rabbeted guides. Keep in mind that the drawer is mounted directly under the single-thickness bench top, so the guide is placed alongside the end cleat.

The planter section at the end comprises two boards, 5 inches high, each of which is grooved near the top for the slide cover.

Finishing is best done with dark maple stain, allowed to penetrate deeply into the wood, followed with wax or shellac coat. •

BLACKBOARD FOR CHILDREN

. . . enclosed by hardboard on all sides corrals the chalkdust and keeps the small fry's masterpieces off fresh wallpaper.

THIS children's blackboard is enclosed on all sides, a design that helps to eliminate chalkdust from the floor and discourages little Will or Polly from extending a drawing onto the wallpaper.

It requires only a 2 x 4-ft. piece of tempered hardboard and a bit of any softwood or hardwood on hand. First, trim the hardboard to 21¼ x 47¼ in. on the table saw. Finish it now, with one coat of a non-penetrating sealer such as DuPont Sealer Coater or Co-Ca-Seal (because a penetrating sealer requires several coats in porous hardboard) and then two coats of blackboard paint. Cut the four sides to size, dado the grooves and corner rabbets as shown, and assemble with glue and nails at the corners. •

MATERIALS USED IN EXAMPLE

1 pc.—¼" x 24" x 48" tempered Allwood—blackboard
1 pc.—¾" x 4¼" x 22" pine—two sides
1 pc.—¾" x 3" x 47¼" pine—bottom
1 pc.—¾" x 1¼" x 47¼" pine—top
Glue and 6d finish nails

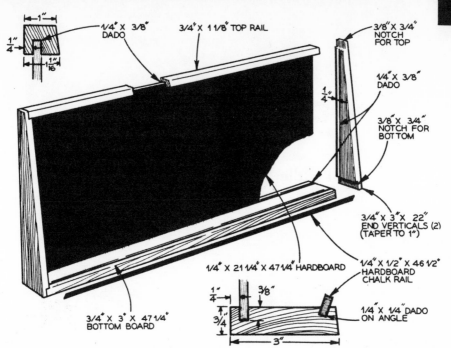

1" 1/4" X 3/8" DADO

1/4"

1/16"

3/4" X 1 1/8" TOP RAIL

3/8" X 3/4" NOTCH FOR TOP

1/4"

1/4" X 3/8" DADO

3/8" X 3/4" NOTCH FOR BOTTOM

3/4" X 3" X 22" END VERTICALS (2) (TAPER TO 1")

1/4" X 21 1/4" X 47 1/4" HARDBOARD

1/4" X 1/2" X 46 1/2" HARDBOARD CHALK RAIL

3/4" X 3" X 47 1/4" BOTTOM BOARD

1/4"

3/8"

3/4"

3"

1/4" X 1/4" DADO ON ANGLE

Below. Joinery, this project, is done entirely with dado blade. First you rabbet the ends, as shown.

Below. With your dado set for cut of 1/4", run all four pieces at same time for hardboard back.

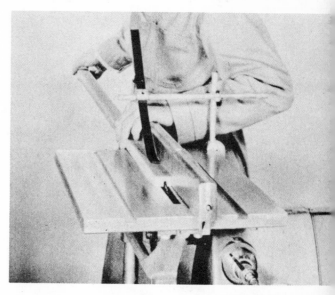

Tilt table to 20 degrees to run 1/4" groove for chalk holder which is from waste of 24" width.

Note that universal hold-down is set ahead of—not directly over—the blade in all operations.

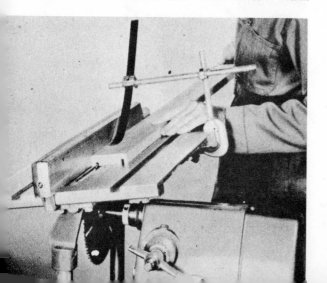

PEEPER

Paddle boat for kids has glass-bottom viewer.

WIDE PLEXIGLAS STRIP on bottom gives clear view of underwater marvels through viewer.

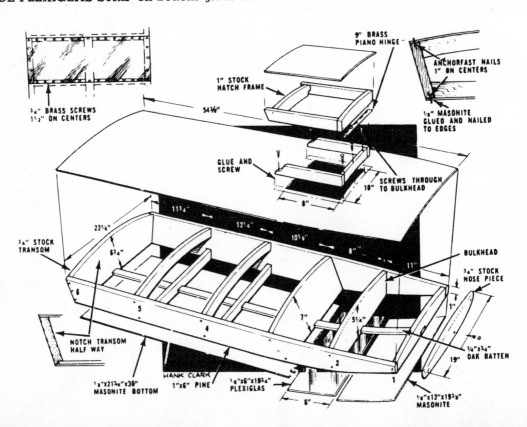

JUNIOR frogmen (and girl tadpoles, too) will have a splashing good time cavorting on this paddle boat with its Plexiglas window for underwater observations . . . and it can be built in an evening.

Start by marking off the 1x6 pine stock as shown in the drawing. Lay out the bulkheads and frame members, then saw all pieces to size as shown in the drawing. Next, glue and screw the side panels to the cross frames. Install the ¼x¾-inch oak center batten as shown, notching it through each frame and half-through the transom. Plane the edges of frames and side pieces to insure a snug fit for the Plexiglas and the top and bottom Tempered Masonite panels.

Fix the window to the bottom of the hatch well with ¾-inch brass wood screws on 1½-inch centers. Drill and countersink the Plexiglas before bedding it in an even layer of waterproof glue, then secure it with wood screws. The deck and bottom panels are similarly glued but are nailed with Anchorfast boat nails. When the glue dries, plane edges flush with sides.

Saw out the hatch opening above the Plexiglas and glue and screw the hatch coamings in place. The hatch cover is ⅛-inch Tempered Masonite over a ¾-inch pipe frame; attach it along the forward edge with a brass piano hinge. Secure the nose block in place with screws and shape it to the contours of the boat. Fill screw holes with plastic wood and sand smooth. Fasten the half-round gunwales in place, then apply a good undercoating to the boat followed by a finish coat of marine paint. •

FRAME SIZES can be accurately figured by checking drawing (below) with chart.

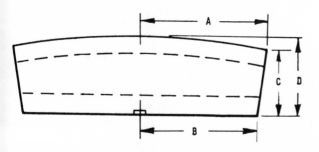

STATION NO.	DIMENSIONS IN INCHES			
	A	B	C	D*
1	9½	9⅜	1⅛	1¾
2	10⅜	9-11/16	4½	5¼
3	10¾	9⅞	5¾	7
4	11-1/16	10-13/16	1⅛	2
5	11⅛	11	1-1/16	2
6	11⅛	10-3/16	5¾	6¾

*OVER-ALL DIMENSION: USE TO SELECT BOARD WIDTH.

LIGHTWEIGHT and bouyant, Peeper can be paddled with hands and feet as shown here.

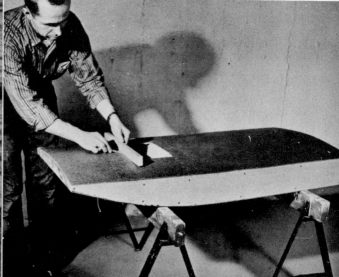

MASONITE panels bend easily to form deck. Here hatch frame is marked for curved cut.

L. DORADO

By Glen L. Witt, N.A.

Popular 13-footer combines class with speed.

MAXIMUM practical power for the L. Dorado is 40 hp., but does well with smaller units.

HERE IS ONE OF THE most advance-styled, modern boats available to the builder. The L. Dorado's overall length of 13 feet, with an extremely wide beam of 68 inches, provides safe, proven performance. The flowing tails not only set a styling standard but also prove functional in keeping the motor and the aft passengers free from spray. The split back front seat allows quick and easy access between the cockpits.

The L. Dorado is intended for motors to 40 horsepower. If the builder anticipates using more power, a 15-foot model (in plans) is available for the larger motors.

Because of the unusual design of the L. Dorado, it is suggested that the builder carefully follow the sequence of the photographs and instructions, even though he has had previous building experience.

GENERAL SPECIFICATIONS

All framing and longitudinal lumber may be white oak, Philippine mahogany or Sitka spruce. All plywood used should be edge stamped DFPA. The planking should be full marine grade, while floorboards, gussets, etc. may be standard ex-

FRAMES are mounted on a box-like building form, leveled fore, aft and across.

SPRINGING initial sheer clamp in place. For ease in bending, two pieces are used.

SECOND LAMINATION of the sheer is glued and screwed through both into the frames.

SQUARE is used for fairing frame. All surfaces must be beveled to receive skin.

MEMBERS of framework being coated with glue. Mastic optional at the water joints.

AFTER FITTING bottom planking to sides, screw into chine. Wet burlap aids bending.

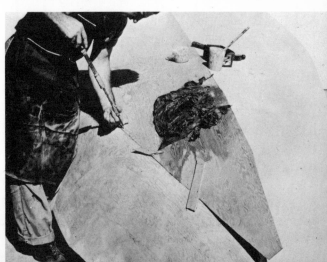

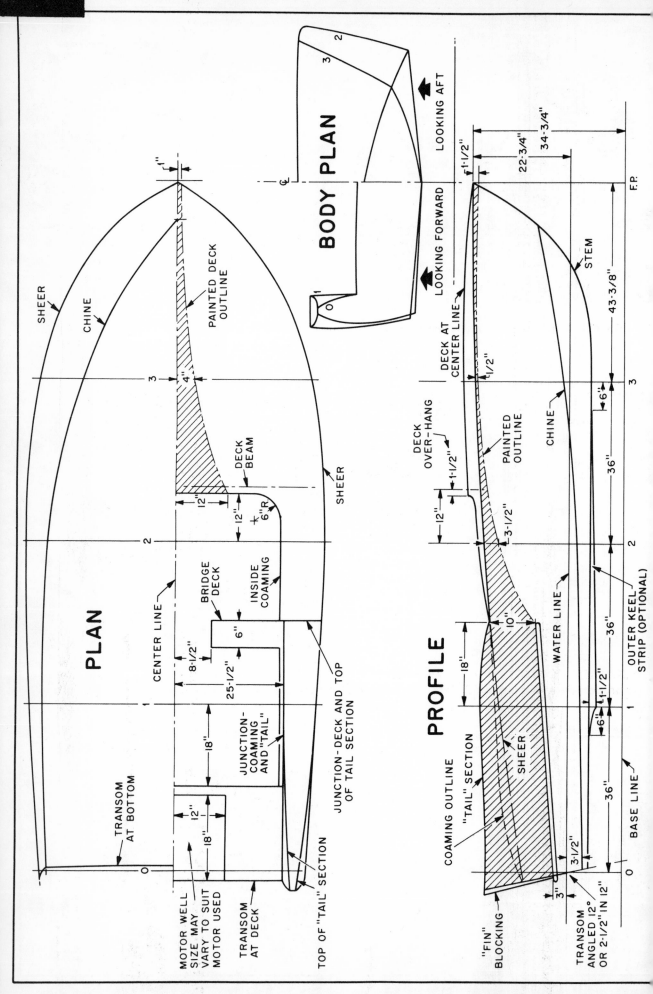

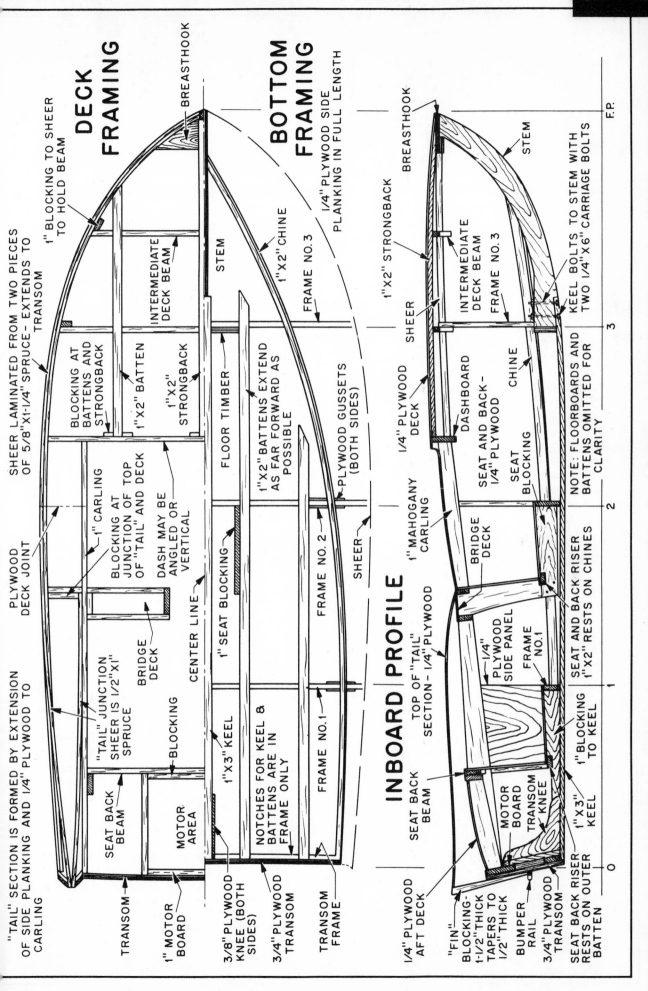

DECK FRAMING

BREASTHOOK

1" BLOCKING TO SHEER TO HOLD BEAM

SHEER LAMINATED FROM TWO PIECES OF 5/8"X1-1/4" SPRUCE- EXTENDS TO TRANSOM

INTERMEDIATE DECK BEAM

BLOCKING AT BATTENS AND STRONGBACK

1"X2" BATTEN

1"X2" STRONGBACK

1" CARLING

BLOCKING AT JUNCTION OF TOP OF "TAIL" AND DECK

DASH MAY BE ANGLED OR VERTICAL

PLYWOOD DECK JOINT

"TAIL" JUNCTION SHEER IS 1/2"X1" SPRUCE

BRIDGE DECK

CENTER LINE

BLOCKING

"TAIL" SECTION IS FORMED BY EXTENSION OF SIDE PLANKING AND 1/4" PLYWOOD TO CARLING

TRANSOM

1" MOTOR BOARD

SEAT BACK BEAM

MOTOR AREA

BOTTOM FRAMING

1/4" PLYWOOD SIDE PLANKING IN FULL LENGTH

STEM

1"X2" CHINE

FRAME NO. 3

FLOOR TIMBER

1"X2" BATTENS EXTEND AS FAR FORWARD AS POSSIBLE

PLYWOOD GUSSETS (BOTH SIDES)

1" SEAT BLOCKING

FRAME NO. 2

SHEER

FRAME NO.1

1"X3" KEEL

NOTCHES FOR KEEL & BATTENS ARE IN FRAME ONLY

3/8" PLYWOOD KNEE (BOTH SIDES)

3/4" PLYWOOD TRANSOM

TRANSOM FRAME

INBOARD PROFILE

TOP OF "TAIL" SECTION- 1/4" PLYWOOD

1" MAHOGANY CARLING

SEAT BACK BEAM

1/4" PLYWOOD AFT DECK

"FIN" BLOCKING- 1-1/2" THICK TAPERS TO 1/2" THICK

BUMPER RAIL

3/4" PLYWOOD TRANSOM

SEAT BACK RISER RESTS ON OUTER BATTEN

MOTOR BOARD

TRANSOM KNEE

1"X3" KEEL

1" BLOCKING TO KEEL

BREASTHOOK

STEM

INTERMEDIATE DECK BEAM

FRAME NO. 3

1"X2" STRONGBACK

SHEER

1/4" PLYWOOD DECK

DASHBOARD

BRIDGE DECK

CHINE

SEAT AND BACK- 1/4" PLYWOOD

SEAT BLOCKING

1/4" PLYWOOD SIDE PANEL

FRAME NO.1

SEAT AND BACK RISER 1"X2" RESTS ON CHINES

KEEL BOLTS TO STEM WITH TWO 1/4"X6" CARRIAGE BOLTS

NOTE: FLOORBOARDS AND BATTENS OMITTED FOR CLARITY

F.P.

3

2

1

0

FITTING carling and tail section into place. Fit carefully for extra strength.

DECKING is scribed in place and nailed down. Interior is completed before decking.

terior grade. All fastenings should be bronze or hot dipped galvanized. Brass is not advised, except in nonstress areas, due to the tendency to fracture under strain. If you have trouble locating the proper sized fastenings "Glen L" can furnish kits that include all of the required screws and nails. All surfaces should be glued with resorcinol or urea-resin glue. Nails are to be the Anchorfast or the annular thread type. The frames are fabricated from 1-inch material. At the junction, use at least five 1-inch nails in each leg. Frames No. 1 and No. 2 are formed by a bottom member in single width, while frame No. 3 incorporates the bottom and side member in one part, held together with a floor timber.

BUILDING INSTRUCTIONS

TRANSOM: The transom is cut from ¾-inch plywood to the given shape. The entire transom is framed in 1-inch material. Notches are cut from the framework, but not into the transom plywood. Screw the framework to the transom with 1½-inch No. 8 screws, spaced 6 inches apart.

STEM: Stem, breasthook and transom knee are all fabricated from two layers of ¾-inch plywood to the shape shown. The breasthook is so designed as to lock notch around the stem and rest on top.

SETTING UP: The bottom is built bottom side up on the indicated building form. With the longitudinal setup members being level athwartships and lengthwise, the frames are carefully aligned with a level to be completely vertical and on their centerline. The stem and breasthook assembly is screwed to the No. 3 frame and blocked to its proper position.

KEEL: The 1x3-inch keel is bolted to the stem with ¼-inch carriage bolts and screwed to each frame and transom with 2-inch No. 10 screws.

BATTENS: The 1x2-inch battens are located per the notches indicated in each of the frames and transom and fastened with 2-inch No. 10 screws.

CHINE: The chine is notched into the frames and tapered to fit against the stem. This 1x2-inch member is fastened to each mating point with 2-inch No. 10 screws.

SHEER: The sheer is built up from two laminations of ⅝x1¼-inch spruce. One lamination is put on at a time to simplify the bending.

FAIRING: The hull framework must be faired or beveled so that the planking will mate to all surfaces. Take care in the fairing. Be sure the lines are clean, even sweeps. To assure a proper performing boat the longitudinal lines in the aft portion of the boat must be straight lines.

PLANKING SIDE: The sides are planked with ¼-inch plywood in full length panels. If shorter panels are desired, they should be joined as shown in the drawings. A panel is leaned against the side of the boat and roughly scribed to shape. After fitting, the panel is fastened with 1-inch No. 8 screws, to the chine, transom and stem spaced about 3 inches apart.

BOTTOM PLANKING: The bottom planking is either ¼-inch or ⅜-inch plywood. The ⅜-inch will only be required if the hull will be used exceptionally roughly. Fit the panel in place carefully along the portion that will butt join with the side planking. Other areas may be left long or trimmed after the planking is fastened in place.

OUTER KEEL: The outer keel or aluminum fin is optional, as shown in the drawings.

SPRAY RAIL: An optional but desirable feature is a spray rail that covers the joint of the side and bottom planking. The hull is then removed from the form and turned right side up. Par for this operation is usually half a day, while neighbors and friends make comments and the builder

PLAN SET AND FULL SIZE

patterns will greatly simplify construction of this boat, L. DORADO. Please consult your PLANS REFERENCE LISTING for the exact source and price. Refer to Plan Number 100.

takes pride in showing the shape of the hull to this point.

CARLING: The carling is cut to shape from the pattern given. It is fastened in place along the inside of the frame side members. The inner tail covering, ¼-inch plywood, is preassembled to this member.

TAIL SHEER: The tail sheer clamps are cut from 1-inch spruce to a width of 1 inch. These members extend from the carling and sheer to the transom.

DECK FRAMEWORK: The dashboard beam is cut from 1-inch mahogany and is fitted between the sheers. The intermediate deck beams, strongbacks and deck battens are next fitted into position as indicated in the drawings.

FORWARD DECK: The decking can either be mahogany or Douglas fir if the hull is to be painted. The decking is nailed on with 1-inch nails spaced 2 inches apart. The motor well and bridge deck area is fabricated per the drawings indicated. The rear seat and floorboards may be ¼-inch or ⅜-inch plywood.

FIBERGLASSING: The hull can be fiberglassed or not, as the builder desires. Fir plywood has a habit of checking and, of course, fiberglass will eliminate this problem. Kits for fiberglassing the L. Dorado are available from "Glen L." These contain cloth, resin, squeegee, brush, acetone and instructions.

POWER: The motor used can be almost any practical size to a maximum of 40 horsepower. Such a motor will provide a speed of 35+ miles per hour. With varying passenger and motor weights you may find it necessary to shift the tank and/or battery forward. It is also permissible to shift the front seat forward to gain more room.

CONCLUSION: Building the L. Dorado is a lot of fun. It attracts attention wherever it goes, and when built as described, she goes like a bomb. Best of luck, and send us some photos on the finished product. •

BILL OF MATERIALS

With the Frame Kit, the following are the required materials for the basic hull. If the Frame Kit is not purchased, add the materials on the full size drawings of the frames. All lumber noted allows length for fitting. All widths are actual sizes. All thicknesses given are actual except those listed as 1″, these will be standard four quarters material finished as full as possible.

D. F. PLYWOOD
Planking, bottom—1 piece ¼″x4′x14′
Planking, side—2 pieces ¼″x30″x14′
Seats, inner tails, floorboards, etc.—
  2 pieces ¼″x4′x8′

MAHOGANY OR D. F. PLYWOOD
Decking—2 pieces ¼″x3′x8′

SPRUCE OR MAHOGANY
Keel—1 piece 1″x2″x9′6″
Chines—2 pieces 1″x2″x14′
Battens—2 pieces 1″x2″x10′
  2 pieces 1″x2″x8′
  2 pieces 1″x2″x7′6″
Outer keel (optional alum. fin)—
  1 piece 1″x2″x7′
Seat-back beam—1 piece 1″x4″x4′6″
Strongback—1 piece 1″x2″x6′
Deck battens—2 pieces 1″x2″x4′6″

MAHOGANY
Carling—2 pieces 1″x6″x7′6″
Dashboard beam—1 piece 1″x6″x6′
Seats, well & misc. blocking—approx.
  12 random board feet
Fin blocking—1 piece 2″x6″x18″
Bumper rails—2 pieces 1″x2″x5′

SPRUCE
Sheer clamps—4 pieces ⅝″x1¼″x14′

FASTENINGS: all screws are bronze or hot dipped galvanized iron, all nails refer to annular ring monel or bronze.
2″ #10 F. H. Screws—1 gross
1″ #8 F. H. Screws—5 gross
1½″ #8 F. H. Screws—1 gross
1″ nails—approx. 700 or 2 lbs.
2 galvanized carriage bolts—¼″x5½″
  with washers
Glue: plastic resin "Weldwood", 5 lbs;
  or comparable volume of resorcinol type.

NOTE: Several options are given in building specifications. Builder is advised to use above material list as general guide only checking against specifications.

HUSTLER

By Henry Clark

Speedabout is low in cost, high in performance.

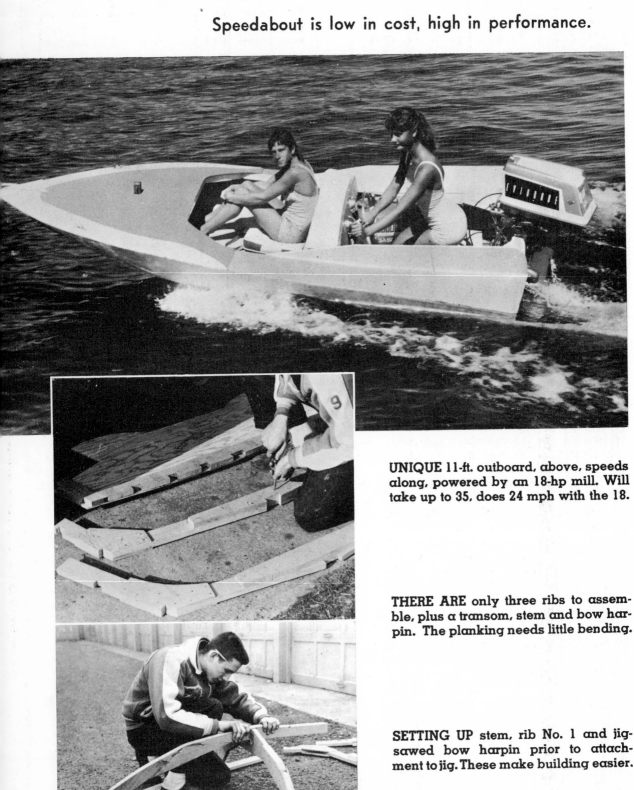

UNIQUE 11-ft. outboard, above, speeds along, powered by an 18-hp mill. Will take up to 35, does 24 mph with the 18.

THERE ARE only three ribs to assemble, plus a transom, stem and bow harpin. The planking needs little bending.

SETTING UP stem, rib No. 1 and jigsawed bow harpin prior to attachment to jig. These make building easier.

ON JIG extra ribs and transom quickly receive chines, sheer and keelson (above).

SIDE PANELS are screwed into place after carefully dressing frame to receive them.

FAIRING STICK bends over battens to test bevels of chine. File to correct.

BOTTOM PANELS are glued and screwed into place, butting along center of keelson.

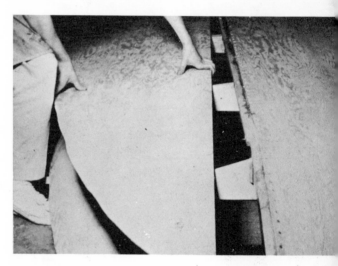

FOR THE MAN or boy who wants the action of the racing gang, at a much lower cost and with easier construction, this boat was designed. After some months of creaming around in my 9-ft. Bubbles, one boy asked for a faster job, one which could carry a few friends along and still go car-top if necessary. With this in mind, the layout yielded a hull as simple as Bubbles', but far roomier, sturdier, and faster. The cost runs from 65 to 75 bucks depending on where you live.

Transom is uniquely braced to take up to 35 hp if the driver knows his stuff, but this driver was content with an 18 hp Evinrude, with remote controls. This drove the boat 30 mph average with an all-purpose prop. Even with a smaller 10 hp on, we clocked 24 mph on our Aqua Meter.

To the looks of a hydro was added the rakish fins which impart high freeboard and ward off splash. And though the ribs are simple, straight rips, the bottom is

semiround, giving a soft ride and rolling turns. Center wheel dash unit is also front seat back rest. Gas tank goes in front when going solo.

Construction is easy in view of the rugged hull obtained, and the test model was put together by a teen boy and his shop teacher, who had never built a boat. There are only three ribs to assemble, a transom, stem, and bow harpin. The plywood needs little bending on this frame, making for building ease. First thing is to obtain the rib stock. Lay the pieces out on the full size drawings, and assemble with gussets and glue over the joints, then notch.

The ¼-inch ply transom blank is laid out, and its oak frames glued to it, then screwed on from the back. Notches for battens and chines are cut first before gluing to transom. Motor clamps come later. Stem is cut to form on band saw, or with many passes on a table saw, and joined to forefoot with web at the joint.

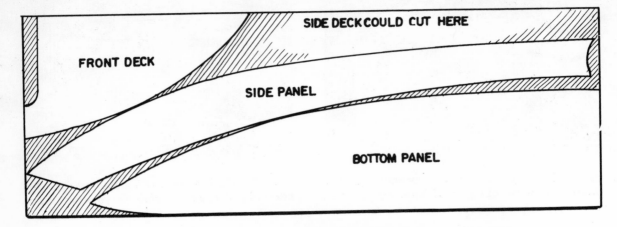

SIDE DECK COULD CUT HERE

FRONT DECK

SIDE PANEL

BOTTOM PANEL

TWO 1/4"X 4'X 14' WELDWOOD MARINE PLYWOOD YIELDS ALL PANELS

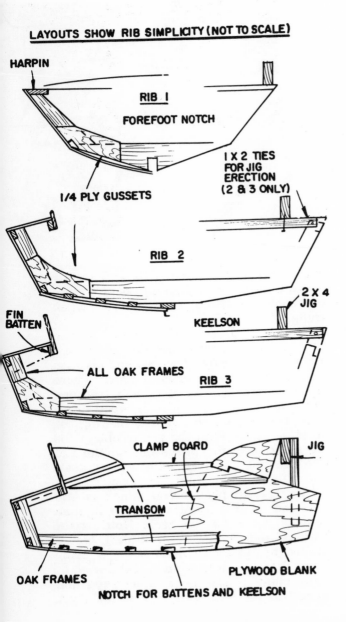

LAYOUTS SHOW RIB SIMPLICITY (NOT TO SCALE)

HARPIN

RIB 1

FOREFOOT NOTCH

1 X 2 TIES
FOR JIG
ERECTION
(2 & 3 ONLY)

1/4 PLY GUSSETS

RIB 2

2 X 4
JIG

FIN
BATTEN

KEELSON

ALL OAK FRAMES

RIB 3

CLAMP BOARD

JIG

TRANSOM

OAK FRAMES

PLYWOOD BLANK

NOTCH FOR BATTENS AND KEELSON

Bow harpin is simple fir stock, again formed with band or table saw to curve. Two halves are joined with plywood gusset at front. These few simple parts are now set up on the jig, which is two 2 by 4 lengths laid endwise on the ground (or on blocks if you wish). Stand Rib 1 on harpin, and stem into the notch, with two screws into the harpin front. Set this assembly onto the jig, securing with two nails through harpin into jig. Position squarely.

On Ribs 2 and 3, screw a 1x2-inch tie strip across their tops to support them on the jig. Stand transom at rear, and lay the keelson into all its notches, right to transom. Then secure transom at its 5-inch incline, with braces down to jig. Space ribs and get them 90 degrees to keelson, then run screws through keelson into each rib and transom. Use glue. Sheer rail goes on next by screwing it to harpin edges first, horizontally, then springing back into other rib notches and transom, with a screw in each. Chine rail goes on by screwing to transom notch first then bending down past notches to stem. Bevel this end for lay against stem side, and screw it here about ½ inch back from edge. This ½-inch area will be beveled for planking. Before cutting any plywood for fitting, plane a bevel along the chine creating a flat area for the bottom plywood to lie on.

To help here, lay the bottom center batten in position across the ribs, then bend a "fairing" stick (any narrow piece of flexible wood) over this batten to touch the keelson, and the chine. Plane away the chine until this stick proves out a flat area. At the harpin sides, considerable angle must be planed for good side panel contact.

Labels: DECK RIB — CHINE — SHEER RAIL — 3/4" STOCK BOW HARPIN — DECK RIB — BOTTOM BATTENS — VOLLRATH WHEEL — REAR CLAMP BOARD — CORNER KNEE — X 4" JIG — KINGPLANK — 1/4 PLYWOOD DECK — 1 — FIN BATTEN — BACK REST — SIDE DECKS — 1/4 PLY FLOOR — JIG LINE — EVINRUDE 18 — 2 — MAHOGANY FINS — 3 — K STEM — 2" NO. 8 IN ALL RIBS — SHEER NOTCHED INTO HARPIN — KEELSON NOTCHED INTO FOREFOOT — 1/4 PLY BOTTOM & SIDES — OUTER KEEL — (AFTERPLANE)

Now cut the side panels because they go on first. Cut them out in either of two ways. One, using the diagram on the large scale plans, or by clamping the entire ply panel on the hull, with one edge down keelson's center line. Scribe outline of bottom panel, and cut out, leaving the side panels free for scribing. These are clamped on, drilled for screws every 2 inches at chine, and 4 inches at sheer, trimmed, removed, glued up with Weldwood resin glue, then replaced with a few clamps and pilot screws. Be sure panels lie in good contact by again using the fairing stick. If only the rear portion lies correctly, cut the 2 by 4 back to under the harpin. After the side is on, plane chine edge to angle already planed on the frame chine. Now add the other bottom battens, notching them about ½ inch into ribs, or as shown on the rib art. With the center one raised, and two part-way down, this accounts for the semiround bottom you will obtain, a bonus for little effort.

Bottom plywood must be screwed to all these battens, as well as to keelson, chines, and transom. Lay bottom panel in place,

clamped to keelson center line, and put in a few pilot screws. Plane away edges to conform to sides and stem, and drill all other holes, without countersinking, every 2 inches along the keelson, chines, transom, and stem; every 5 inches along the bottom battens. Remove panel, swab on creamy Weldwood mix along all drilled surfaces, replace plywood with the pilot screws, then proceed to drive in all other ⅞-inch No. 7 screws, driving them flush with the plywood surface. Countersinking leaves too many pits to fill, and weakens the holding power of the screws.

Bottom extends some 5 inches aft of transom as afterplane. This may remain or be cut according to porpoising action later. When gluing up bottom lay ½-inch-wide strips of linen into the glue along chines, outside screw holes, and along transom, which will help spread the glue better. Add the short outer keel now, or later. Now you can flip the hull and remove the jig and the rib ties. Now you will see the fine, safe beam your small hull has. Cut and round the deck dash first, and install it to help keep the rib spread. Next cut and

THOUGH SMALL, 11-ft. Hustler easily carries a passenger or two while towing a water skier.

SCREWING FIN brace to transom, left. Note rear clamp board on transom and bottom after-plane.

BILL OF MATERIALS

WHITE OAK

¾"x5"x30"	Rib-1
¾"x3"x78"	Rib-1-Transom
¾"x2½"x70"	Ribs-Transom
¾"x4"x97"	Ribs
¾"x3"x52"	Knees
2"x3"x72"	Stem
1"x2½"x60"	Sister Keelsons

MARINE PLYWOOD

¼"x20"x60"	Transom Blank
¼"x24"x48"	Gussets
¼"x4'x12' (2)	Planking
¼"x4'x5'	Floor

PHILIPPINE MAHOGANY

¾"x2½"x8'	Keelson
¾"x5"x11'	Ripped for Chines-Battens
¾"x10"x8'	Sheers-Battens
¾"x4"x36"	Transom Clamp

¾"x7"x88"	Wheel Dash-Rest
¾"x15"x20"	Rear Motor Clamp
½"x12"x9'	Fins

FIR-SPRUCE

¾"x3½"x12'	Bow Harpin
¾"x2"x14'	Fin Battens
¾"x5"x60"	Deck Dash
¾"x2"x52"	King Plank

SCREWS

⅞" No. 7	Brass (4-Gross)
¾" No. 6	Brass (2-Dozen)
½"	Galv. Brads 1 Lb. (For Gussets)
2" No. 8	Galv. (3-Dozen)
2" No. 10	Galv. (1-Doz.)
Weldwood Resin Glue 3 Lb.	

KINGPLANK is shown being screwed down to dash board. "Fair" for deck planking.

FRONT DECK butts on kingplank, with single piece to stem (alternative on p. 38).

form the top motor clamp board, and screw in place with glue. Notch it first to receive the two corner braces, or knees, which are made now and screwed in to notches and to sheer rail with 3-inch No. 10 screws, predrilled. This unique bracing makes a very strong transom, and permits use of heavier motors. Now add the two fin battens reaching from dash to transom, notching under the corner knees. Pull these into curve with two braces over to sheer. Plane the tops of these battens to conform to rake outward of the side decks. Test for flatness with stick. Now add the side decks before fins, cutting from the plywood scrap area. One-half-inch mahogany would be impressive, but also somewhat heavy, as we learned from Bubble. Secure decks with ¾-inch No. 6 screws every 4 inches. Cut the deck out last, after adding the center kingplank. If deck material is short, butt with other scrap, or improvise to taste. Before putting down deck, you might apply paint, or other preservative to the bare insides for longer weathering resistance. The fins are cut from ½-inch mahogany now, shaped, and clamped to the batten's faces after applying glue. Note that fins rake outward to some 90 degrees to the decks, and offer more cockpit room and a good splash fence. You cannot keep water out without them, as aft end sets low in hydro fashion. Wheel dash is now added along with back rest and plywood topping. These secure to small blocks glued to inside faces of fins. Drill for wheel drum and in-

stall Vollrath Viking wheel and cables with only four pulleys. For floor, plywood lays on fir blocks glued atop the bottom battens. Secure plywood to these. Do not sand the outside of the hull as it is presanded. Only sand where your glue oozes, etc. Add Firzite filler and paint with exterior enamels of your choice. Add rub rails of oak, or an aluminum bead. Vollrath stainless steel hardware finishes it. Lights are optional. Evinrude Simplex remote controls, 7 ft. long, allow forward facing and control, so you can kneel while speeding along in your new hot rod, flying low, and even pulling a skier or two. •

SPECIFICATIONS

Length	11 ft.
Beam	5 ft.
Depth	21 in.
Freeboard	18 in.
Weight	200 lbs.

LARGE SCALE PLANS

with full size half ribs will greatly simplify construction of this boat, **HUSTLER**. Please consult your **PLANS REFERENCE LISTING** for exact source and price. Refer to Plan Number 101.

WETBACK

By Hal Kelly

A Class B & C Hydro that you can rely on for lead-the-pack performance every time.

WETBACK is primarily designed for stock outboard racing motors, for both class "B" and class "C." This is not an off-the-drawingboard plan. Wetback was designed, built and raced, and is a proven trophy winner, a truly tested plan. She is a fast, safe, rough water hydro. On ideal racing water she runs like a bomb, with her sponsons barely tapping the water. On rough water she really comes into her own; on a two-foot chop she can really cook. Highly maneuverable, she can turn on a dime. For the fellow who wants to get the most speed out of his pleasure motor, Wetback is a good bet. The transom height must be increased to about 16 inches for a motor with a standard lower unit. Wetback will weigh under 115 lbs. with hardware if built with the materials listed.

First, I suggest spending a few hours studying the plans and the photographs of her in construction. Total cost of materials will vary. Depending on where you live and the grade of plywood you use, she could cost anywhere from $75 to $135.

After accumulating the stock listed in the bill of materials, you are ready to start on the ribs. Due to space limitations only half of each rib is shown, but since the ribs are symmetrical, each side being the same shape, this will offer no problem. Cut out all of your rib components and place them on the full size rib drawings using ¾-inch No. 16 Anchorfast nails to secure the ¼-inch plywood to the frames. A piece of thin wax paper or cellophane under the ribs will keep the glue off your plans. Weldwood glue is used throughout. Some changes were made in the plans that differ slightly from details in the photos. Stringers were not found necessary on the chines, and all the afterplane on the transom was removed. Stick to the plans for placement of all lightening holes.

Rib No. 1 is made from ¼-inch thick plywood. Cut the ¼-inch wide slits in it where indicated on the plan. These engage the main girders. The small blocks that the battens, etc., are attached to, are glued and fastened to the rib with two ¾-inch No. 16 Anchorfast nails (this same size Anchorfast nail is used throughout the boat). Rib No. 2 is cut from ⅝-inch thick Sitka spruce, ¼-inch plywood gussets are glued and fastened in place with Anchorfast nails in the position indicated on the plan. The holes are cut into the plywood with a circle or fly cutter before attaching to the frame. The fly cutter is almost a must in building this boat what with the great number of different sized holes being cut in the ribs and girders. It is best used in a drill press but can be handled quite nicely in a ¼-inch electric drill. The middle plywood deck support that is attached to Rib No. 2 is put in place when the hydro is turned over to finish the topside.

Rib No. 3 is assembled similar to Rib No. 2. The Sitka spruce is also ⅝ inch thick. Rib No. 4 is made of ½-inch thick Honduras mahogany (¾-inch thick Sitka spruce can replace this). The whole rib is backed with ¼-inch plywood. Note that four holes are cut in the mahogany, and two in the plywood. This plywood forms the back of the sponson, and is glued and fastened with Anchorfast nails. Rib No. 5 and No. 6 are identical except where they meet the main girder which also forms the cockpit coaming. Three-fourths-inch thick Sitka spruce is used as the deck beam with ¼-inch plywood gussets glued, nailed for support.

The transom is made up of two individual pieces which are attached separately to the girders. The transom framing is ¾-inch thick Sitka spruce, with five holes cut into it. It must be carefully notched to receive the battens and chines. The ¼-inch thick plywood is cut a bit oversize. Glued and nailed to the transom frame, this plywood unit is carefully trimmed to size as indicated on the plan. Note side view as to the proper angle on the bottom. This transom should be ten degrees off vertical. The other part of the transom, the motor mount, is made up of 1 piece of ¾-inch thick plywood with ¼-inch plywood pieces glued to each side. Cut this to the size indicated in the plan. Remember to cut the slight angle necessary where the transom mount engages the main girders for a good snug fit.

Main girders: This is the heart of your boat and everything sprouts off it like the branches of a tree. Both girders must be the same and so are cut together with all necessary holes cut into them. Check

GIRDER BEAMS are set up on jig, transom to be glued and screwed to motor mount.

BOW PIECE clamped in place. Note notches for battens in ribs for the tunnel shape.

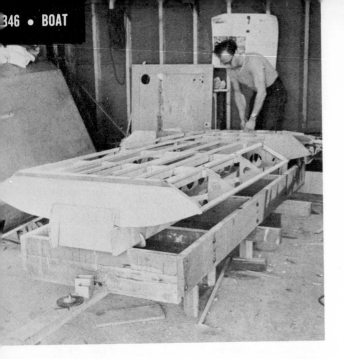

ALL RIBS, battens, stringers in place. Next come sponson battens. Fair them first.

STERN VIEW of topside construction, no afterplane necessary. Varnish inside now.

profile drawing of the girder for correct placement of lightening holes, etc. Mark where you will notch the girders for all the ribs. Cut the notches for Rib No. 1 only, and slip Rib No. 1 into the girders. The motor mount part of the transom is temporarily fastened at the proper angle. Take two 2 x 3's; stand on edge at same angle the girders are running; slip the girders over the 2 x 3's so that they straddle them. This unit is carefully trued up. Then level and square the girders and 2 x 3's in relation to each other. Fasten the 2 x 3's to the base and clamp the girders to them. Take Rib No. 1 and motor mount off the girders. Glue and permanently fasten them to the girders, Rib No. 1 with glue blocks and 1-inch wire brads. Fasten the motor mount with glue and Anchorfast nails spaced about 1 inch apart.

Carefully cut the notches in the girders and fit the rest of the ribs in place, checking the rib plan for proper depth, and girder profile for placement. All ribs are fastened with glue blocks, 1-inch wire brads and glue to the girders. Small details can be well clarified by a careful study of the step by step photos of Wetback in construction. The transom is carefully fitted, glued and screwed with 1½-inch No. 8 screws to the motor mount. The back of the girders are glued and nailed to the transom at the motor well. After the ribs and coaming braces are in place the battens are glued and screwed in place with 1¼-inch No. 8 screws, leaving them a little longer than necessary at the bow.

The chines are next. The bottom angle

on the chines can be cut on the table saw so that no fairing will be necessary. These are glued and screwed in place to the ribs. The bow is made up of three ¼-inch by ¾-inch strips of spruce. Cut the battens and chines to the proper angle and length, using one of the bow strips as a guide. All three strips are coated with glue on both sides, except the outside strip. They are grouped together while the glue is wet, bent and nailed in place at the battens, chines, and ribs. The bow is clamped together every few inches with "C" clamps.

The stringers are glued to the ribs and held in place with glue blocks. Screw the battens to the stringers with 1¼-inch No. 8 screws. The sheers are also cut on a table saw to the proper angle of the chine and deck so that no fairing is necessary at this point. The inside of the sponsons are next. Study plan views and rib drawings for shape and position. The other sponson chine is next, running from Rib No. 4 to bow. The fin brace is glued and screwed to Rib No. 4 and No. 5 with 1¼-inch No. 8 screws.

Most of the fairing necessary will be around the sponson and a little at the bow. This takes more patience than skill and has to be carefully faired so that the plywood planking will seat on all bearings evenly. Frequent checking with an accurate straightedge will be a big help. On any curved surface, be sure that the curve is smooth. Check the bottom for hooks or rockers, especially the last two feet. Make sure that it is flat and straight. The bottom, starting from Rib No. 4 toward the front,

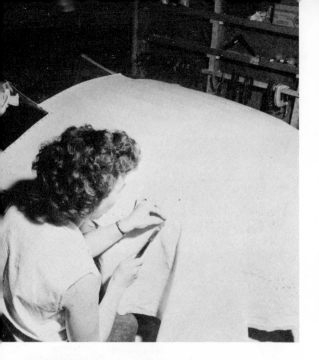

FABRIC decking almost all tacked in position. Give six coats of dope before painting.

FINISHED sponson. Note lip where sides and bottom meet fades to nothing at front.

FRONT view of sponson. Correct angle and workmanship at this point are important.

GAS tank held by shock cord. The ⅛-in. plywood is hatch cover, with twist catches.

has a hollow or tunnel built right into it.

The ¼-inch thick plywood non-trip chines are fitted next. They run from Rib No. 4 to the transom. Glue and nail in place with Anchorfast nails. Then the non-trip is carefully faired at the chine. The afterplane of the sponson is next. This is ¾-inch thick mahogany. Fasten to the sponsons with glue and 1¼-inch No. 8

screws. Note that the afterplane is set in ½ inch from the inside of the sponson so that the small air traps may be screwed to them with 1¼-inch No. 8 screws.

The bottom is carefully cut to the correct width to fit between the sponsons and temporarily fastened in place. The bow shape is marked off on the bottom. Also mark off all the battens, etc., so you will

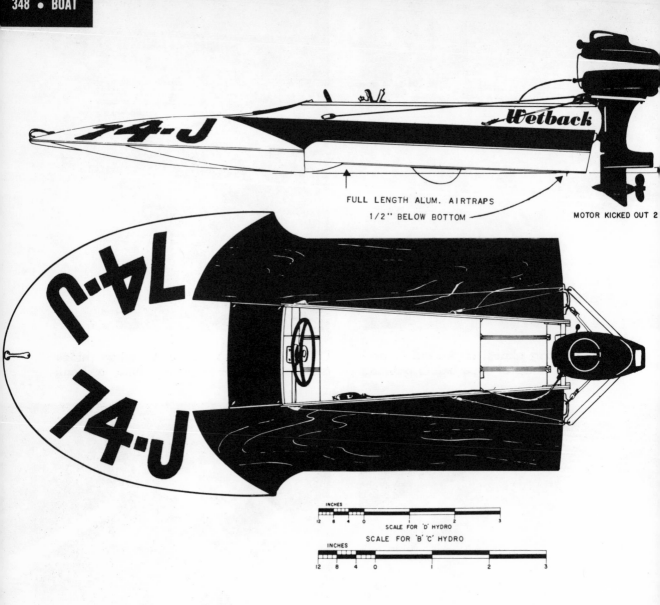

FULL LENGTH ALUM. AIRTRAPS

1/2" BELOW BOTTOM

MOTOR KICKED OUT 2

INCHES

12 8 4 0   1   2   3

SCALE FOR 'D' HYDRO

SCALE FOR 'B' 'C' HYDRO

INCHES

12 8 4 0   1   2   3

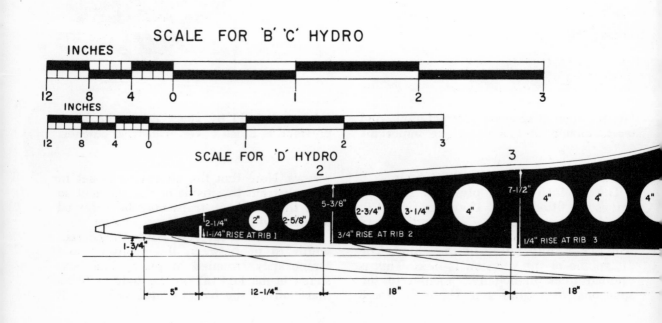

SCALE FOR 'B' 'C' HYDRO

INCHES

12   8   4   0   1   2   3

INCHES

12   8   4   0   1   2   3

SCALE FOR 'D' HYDRO

2-1/4"   2"   2-5/8"   5-3/8"   2-3/4"   3-1/4"   4"   7-1/2"   4"   4"   4"

1-1/4" RISE AT RIB 1   3/4" RISE AT RIB 2   1/4" RISE AT RIB 3

1-3/4"

5"   12-1/4"   18"   18"

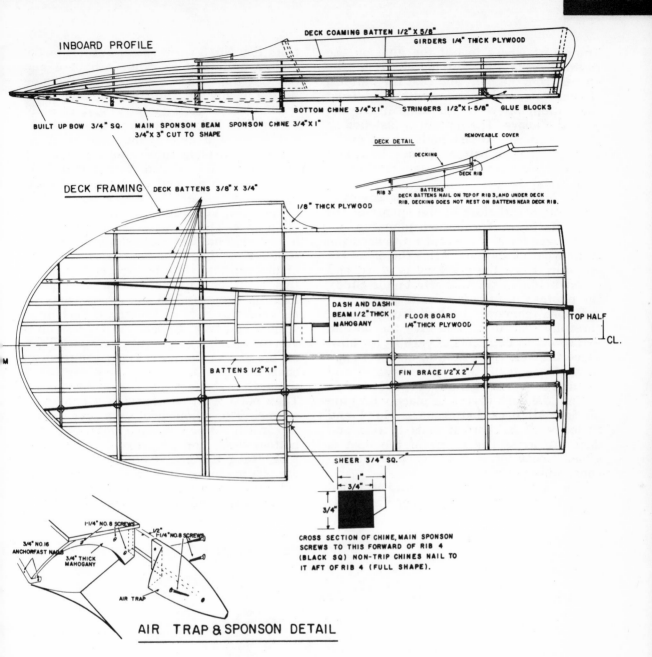

INBOARD PROFILE

DECK COAMING BATTEN 1/2" X 5/8"

GIRDERS 1/4" THICK PLYWOOD

BUILT UP BOW 3/4" SQ.   MAIN SPONSON BEAM   SPONSON CHINE 3/4"X I"
3/4" X 3" CUT TO SHAPE

BOTTOM CHINE 3/4"X I"   STRINGERS 1/2"X I-5/8"   GLUE BLOCKS

DECK DETAIL

REMOVEABLE COVER

DECKING

DECK RIB

RIB 3   BATTENS
DECK BATTENS NAIL ON TOP OF RIB 3, AND UNDER DECK
RIB. DECKING DOES NOT REST ON BATTENS NEAR DECK RIB.

DECK FRAMING   DECK BATTENS 3/8" X 3/4"

1/8" THICK PLYWOOD

DASH AND DASH
BEAM 1/2" THICK
MAHOGANY

FLOOR BOARD
1/4" THICK PLYWOOD

TOP HALF

CL.

BATTENS 1/2"X I"

FIN BRACE 1/2"X 2"

SHEER 3/4" SQ.

1"
3/4"
3/4"

CROSS SECTION OF CHINE, MAIN SPONSON
SCREWS TO THIS FORWARD OF RIB 4
(BLACK SQ) NON-TRIP CHINES NAIL TO
IT AFT OF RIB 4 (FULL SHAPE).

1-1/4" NO.8 SCREWS
1/2"
1/4" NO.8 SCREWS
3/4" NO.16
ANCHORFAST NAILS
3/4" THICK
MAHOGANY
AIR TRAP

AIR TRAP & SPONSON DETAIL

GIRDER PROFILE

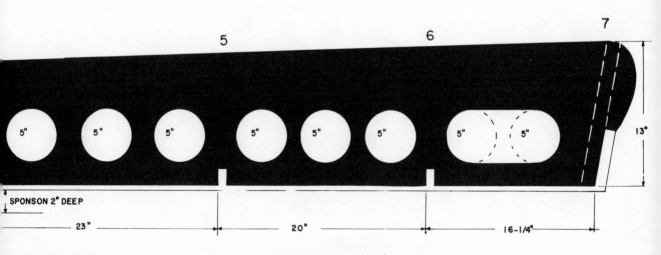

5   6   7

5"   5"   5"   5"   5"   5"   5"   5"

13"

SPONSON 2" DEEP

23"   20"   16-1/4"

know just where to put the glue on the bottom. Take the bottom off. Trim the excess from the bow, and coat the battens, chines, bow, and transom with glue. Coat the bottom where it will come in contact with the above. The bottom is fastened in place with Anchorfast nails about every two inches at all battens, chines, bow, and transom. Countersink the nails and cover with wood dough.

The ¼-inch plywood planking covering the bottom and sides of the sponsons are carefully fitted. The bottom planking extends over the sides except up toward the front where they butt. After the sides are carefully fitted the planking is glued and nailed in place with Anchorfast nails. Study the photos carefully for clarification.

Before removing the hull from the jig, carefully sand down and give the bottom and sponsons two coats of varnish for now. Place the hull right side up on level supports. Once again the hull is leveled and secured so it won't get out of shape. Fasten the middle deck braces in place with glue blocks. All deck battens are glued and nailed with Anchorfast nails to ribs and deck supports. The inside of the boat is given 3 coats of varnish. This is a time-consuming project.

The ⅛-inch plywood decking is glued and nailed in place with Anchorfast nails from Rib No. 3 to transom, but not to the middle deck battens. The dashboard and floorboard are screwed in place, using glue on the dashboard and coaming strip.

The fabric deck is next, and is a lot easier than it looks. It takes me 45 min. to put it on and give it one coat of dope. I use light airplane fabric, but a good grade of muslin could be used. You start tacking in place with a small copper carpet tack, at the top center. At the opposite point at the bow, you stretch tight and put another tack. The next tack is in the middle of one side halfway between the first two tacks, and then another in the middle of the opposite side. Stretch and tack. At this point you have four tacks in place forming a cross. The next four tacks go between the ends of the cross. Each time stretch and tack. Repeat the process until you have the tacks about 1 inch apart. Trim off the excess cloth and apply about seven coats of dope. Do this in a well ventilated room. Give the last coat a good day to dry. Then paint with two coats of a good boat enamel. The whole boat gets seven coats of varnish. After you have wet sanded the bottom well, you are ready for the last coat. Hang the boat from over head and varnish the last coat from underneath; this will give you a real dust free bottom.

Hardware and fin are next. The fin is

WETBACK all set to go, being idled out for her first test run.

BILL OF MATERIALS

BRONZE, MONEL, or EVERDURE FASTENINGS
1 gross of ⅞" no. 8 flathead wood screws
1 gross of 1¼" no. 8 flathead wood screws
4 dozen of 1½" no. 8 flathead wood screws
2 lbs. of ¾" no. 16 Anchorfast nails 950 to lb.
¼ lb. of 19 gauge wire brads

PAINT PRODUCTS
5 lbs. of Weldwood glue
1 lb. of Wood Dough or similar surface filler
1 gal. of Spar varnish
½ gal. of clear Nitrate Dope
½ pint of boat Enamel (color to suit)
50" by 60" Muslin or Aircraft wing fabric

HARDWARE
1 Steering wheel
1 Piece of steering rope 24' long
1 Safety throttle
1 Bowden throttle cable 5' long
1 Racing fin for class B
2 Rear snap pulleys, with snap swivel
2 Steering rope anchor straps
2 Forward steering coaming pulleys
2 Cable clamps
1 Aluminum bow handle
2 Aluminum stern handles
2 12' lengths of ½" half round aluminum

PLYWOOD
Decking 1 sheet of 3 ply waterproof plywood
⅛" x 4' x 7'. Bottom, non-trip chines, sponsons,
girders, gussets rib No. 1 transom and flooring
3 sheets of 5 ply waterproof plywood ¼" x 4'
x 8', or 2 sheets ¼" x 4' x 12' Transom 5 ply
waterproof ¾" x 14" x 14".

SITKA SPRUCE
Sheers—1 piece ¾" x 1" x 10'
Bow piece—3 pieces ¼" x ¾" x 12'
Chine—2 pieces ¾" x 1" x 10'
Battens—4 pieces ½" x 1" x 10'
Bottom stringers—2 pieces ½" x 1⅝" x 5'
Bottom stringers—2 pieces ½" x 1⅝" x 3'
Deck battens—4 pieces ⅜" x ¾" x 10'
Deck battens—7 pieces ⅜" x ¾" x 4'
Deck braces—1 piece ¾" x ¾" x 4'
Deck coaming battens—2 pieces ½" x ⅝" x 7'
Deck beams glue blocks, etc. — 1 piece
  ¾" x 6" x 6'
Frame No. 2—1 piece ⅝" x 2" x 4'
Frame No. 3—1 piece ⅝" x 4¼" x 5'
Frame No. 5 and No. 6—1 piece ¾" x 1⅝" x 8'
Transom—1 piece ¾" x 9" x 4'
Sponson main beam—2 pieces ¾" x 3" x 5'
Sponson chine—2 pieces ¾" x 1" x 4'

HONDURAS MAHOGANY
Frame No. 4—1 piece ½" x 7" x 60"
Sponson afterplane—1 piece ¾" x 8" x 12"
Fin brace dash and dash beam — 1 piece
  ½" x 7" x 5'
Coaming strip—¼" x ¾" x 6'

---

off center to the left 4 inches and the back of the fin is 28 inches from the transom.

To get your racing number join the American Power Boat Association, 700 Canton Ave., Detroit, Michigan. Enclose in the letter a description of your boat and motor; the A.P.B.A. will want to know the make, model and serial number.

Motor angle and height are very important for racing and a motor ⅛ inch too high or low has lost many a race. A Merc motor should run best on the second notch with this boat. Transom height, depending on prop, is around 14 inches. The transom on Wetback is 13½ inches high. You use shim sticks to jack the motor up or down. A marine speedometer is handy to have while making these adjustments. At present I find the stainless steel Kaminc prop is the best. Your best speed is only determined through methodical testing. In order to tell what results you obtain from your changes, make only one alteration at a time. I always run my motor with a full butterfly. In case of a flip it's much safer for you and the other drivers, and will save you from a blown motor.

WETBACK AS A "D" HYDRO
For those who wish to make Wetback into a "D" hydro, I have included scales for ribs, girders, etc. (see plans box, below). This will make her 20 per cent larger. The framing should be 25 per cent heavier, but the decking and planking is the same thickness as the "B", "C". All the construction remains the same. Keep the motor mount on the transom 13½ inches high. •

LARGE SCALE PLANS

with full size rib drawings will greatly simplify construction of this boat, WETBACK. Please consult your PLANS REFERENCE LISTING for the exact source and price. Refer to Plan Number 102.

L. Capitan

By Glen L. Witt, N. A.

This 17-ft. modern inboard runabout has
already set styling standards, is sleek and fast.

FROM THE TIP of the bow to the transom the clean flowing lines of the L.
Capitan give the appearance of action and
motion. The tail section not only gives a
rakish appearance but also serves to keep
the aft passengers dry. If you have ever sat
in the rear of a runabout on a windy day
this feature can really be appreciated.

The L. Capitan is intended to hold any
of almost all of the modern day auto conversions or full marine power plants. The
most important governing factor is that
the overall length of the motor must not
be larger than 40 inches. Motors longer
than this will cause an excessive shaft
angle. The broad beam and clean running
bottom lines enable a variety of power applications. Due to the location of the motor,
directly over the center of buoyancy,
weight differences of the power plant will
not affect performance.

On the following pages the building of
the L. Capitan will be described exactly as

she was built. The builder will find the
construction simpler if he will carefully
read these instructions and study the plans
and photos before starting on the actual
building. The sequence of building, due to
the unusual construction in the tail section,
must be carefully followed.

The L. Capitan is available as Plans and
Patterns (See Plans Box page 357). In
addition to the usual complement of patterns for the frames, stem and transom,
templates are also given for the entire
frame mockup. Also available from Glen
L is the complete Frame Kit that furnishes the frames, transom, stem, breasthook, four tail frames, buttock rail, carling, dash beam, and tail sheers.

Select the material to be used for building the L. Capitan with care. The bill of
materials furnishes the required sizes and
also gives types of lumbers. These may be
varied depending upon the locale the boat
is being built in. Be sure and glue each

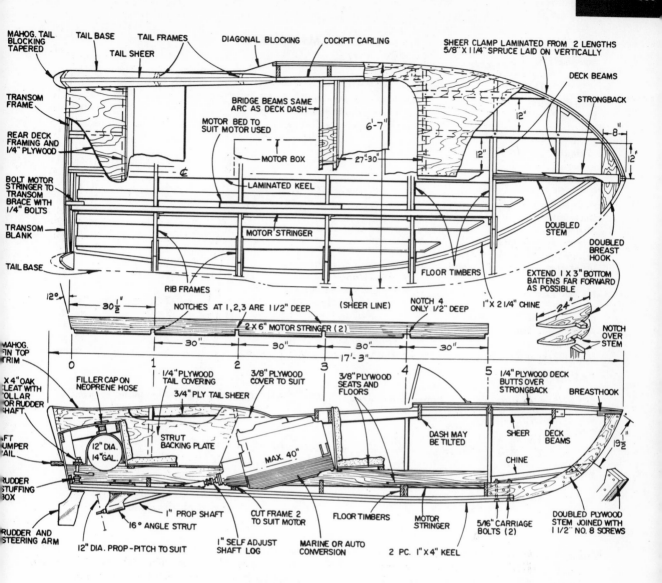

joint in the boat even on the inside. The resorcinol type glue, a liquid and powder type to be mixed together, is the best. The urea resin type is satisfactory and can be used for all work except for gluing oak when submerged in salt water.

FRAMES: The frames are fabricated from one-inch material. At the junction of the side and bottom frame members, a ⅜" gusset is used on both sides of the frame extending a minimum of 6" along each member. On frames No. 1, No. 2 and No. 3, the bottom frame member is in full width from chine to chine. In frames No. 4 and No. 5, the bottom member is in two pieces joined over the centerline by a floor timber member.

TRANSOM: The ⅜" plywood transom is framed in one-inch material. All notches must be cut in the framing members before assembly to the plywood. The bottom frame member is double and the notches placed in this member only for the various

bottom longitudinals. Fit them carefully.

STEM: The stem is fabricated from two layers of ¾" plywood to the shape shown.

BREASTHOOK: The breasthook is cut to shape from ¾" plywood from the template. This is so designed to lock notch around the stem with one layer and bear on top with the other.

MOTOR STRINGERS: The 2"x6" motor stringers are used as the building form. Notches for the frames should be accurate in depth and thickness of lumber taken directly from the frame. Space the notches for the frames per the dimensions given in the drawing.

BUILDING FORM: The motor stringers are set on legs or supports so that they are level both lengthwise and athwartship at a convenient height 24" apart. Align the frames with a chalk line so they are accurately centered and also aligned vertically. The frames are clipped to the motor stringers with angle members or wood

BILL OF MATERIALS

LUMBER:

ITEM	MATERIAL	NO. PCS.	SIZE
Side Planking	D. F. Plywood, Marine Grade AA	2	¼"x3'x18'
Bottom Planking	D. F. Plywood, Marine Grade AA	2	⅜"x3'x16'
Keel	Oak, Mahogany, or Spruce	1	1"x4"x14'
Battens	" " "	2	1"x3"x14'
Battens	" " "	2	1"x3"x13'
Battens	" " "	2	1"x3"x11'
Chine Log	" " "	2	1"x2¼"x18'
Sheer Clamp	" " "	4	⅝"x1¼"x13'
Deck Battens	" " "	2	1"x2"x6'
Deck Battens	" " "	2	1"x2"x4'
Strongback	" " "	1	1"x2"x7'
Intermediate Deck Beam	" " "	1	1"x5"x6'
Bridge and Aft Deck Beam	" " "	3	1"x5"x6'
Inner and Outer Tail Plywood	D. F. Plywood or Mahogany Marine Grade Plywood	2	¼"x4'x8'
Plywood Decking	D. F. Plywood or Mahogany Marine Grade Plywood	2	¼"x4'x8'
Spray Bumper Rail	Mahogany	2	1"x4"x7'
Aft Bumper Rail	Mahogany	1	1"x4"x7'
Motor Stringers	Spruce or D. F. Plywood	2	2"x6'x13'
Misc. Blocking	Mahogany, Spruce, or D. F. Plywood		As required

FASTENINGS:

SCREWS—F. H. Bronze or Hot Dipped Galvanized.
  1" # 8 — 3 Gross
  1¼" # 8 — 4 Gross
  1½" # 8 — 1 Gross
  2" #10 — 2 Gross

BOLTS— Carriage bolts. Hot dipped galvanized.
  ¼"x1½" Carriage Bolts — 12
  ¼"x2½" Carriage Bolts — 28
  ¼"x3" Carriage Bolts — 4

ANGLE CLIPS—Brass, Aluminum, or Iron. ⅛"x2"x2"—10 required, approximately 7" long.

NAILS:— 1"x 109 Min. Diameter— App. ximately 3 lbs.

GLUE— Resorcinol or Urea Resin. 1 Gallon or approximately comparable size 5 lbs.

blocks. The stem, breasthook assembly is located per the dimensions given on the building form and anchor to the floor.

BUTTOCK RAIL: The buttock rail rests on the side members of frames No. 1 and No. 2 and butts to No. 3 and also to the transom. Cut this member from the template from one-inch mahogany or spruce.

KEEL: The keel is built up from two laminations of 1"x4" material or a single 1"x4" member laminated with ⅜" plywood. The keel is fitted into notches in the stem transom and frames.

CHINE LOG: The chine log is 1"x2¼" in single length from stem to transom. Bevel it up forward to match to the side of the frame and notch into each of the frames.

SHEER CLAMP: The junction of the side planking and decking is the sheer clamp. This member is built up from two laminations of ⅝"x1¼" that end between frames No. 2 and No. 3. Notch into the frames and anchor at the breasthook and stem with 2" No. 10 screws.

FAIRING: All of the members must be faired or beveled so that the planking will mate firmly to them. Care should be taken to be sure that the after third of the hull longitudinally is straight and true.

BATTENS: It is preferable to install the 1"x3" bottom battens after fairing. These are notched into the frames the depth of the material spaced per the dimensions indicated on the drawings.

LIMBERS: Limbers are notches along the outboard side of all longitudinals to enable the bilge water to drain aft.

PLANKING SIDE: The sides of the hull are planked with single length panels of ¼" thickness plywood. If full length panels are not available, shorter panels can be spliced as shown in the plan detail. The planking is leaned against the side of the hull and roughly marked around its extremities. It is roughly sawn to shape with a fine tooth hand or power saw, and re-applied permanently to the side of the hull, fastened per the fastening schedule.

BOTTOM PLANKING: The bottom planking is ⅜" in thickness. It is put on in two parts, one on either side of the keel with the two pieces joined over the centerline. Fit the panels similarly to the sides

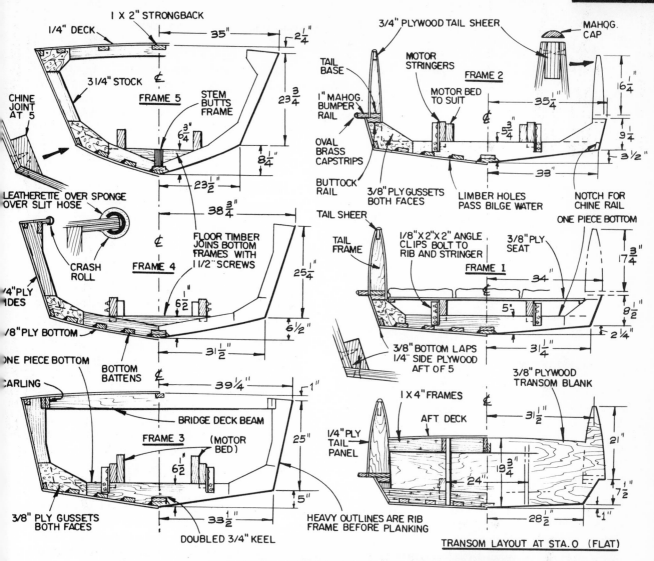

1 X 2" STRONGBACK

1/4" DECK

35"

2¼"

3¼" STOCK

CHINE JOINT AT 5

¢

FRAME 5

STEM BUTTS FRAME

6¾"

23¾"

8¼"

23½"

38¾"

LEATHERETTE OVER SPONGE OVER SLIT HOSE

CRASH ROLL

FRAME 4

¢

FLOOR TIMBER JOINS BOTTOM FRAMES WITH 1½" SCREWS

25¼"

6½"

6½"

1/4" PLY SIDES

3/8" PLY BOTTOM

ONE PIECE BOTTOM

31½"

CARLING

BOTTOM BATTENS

¢

39¼"

1"

BRIDGE DECK BEAM

FRAME 3

(MOTOR BED)

25"

6½"

5"

3/8" PLY GUSSETS BOTH FACES

DOUBLED ¾" KEEL

33½"

3/4" PLYWOOD TAIL SHEER

MOTOR STRINGERS

MAHOG. CAP

TAIL BASE

FRAME 2

1" MAHOG. BUMPER RAIL

MOTOR BED TO SUIT

35¼"

16¼"

OVAL BRASS CAPSTRIPS

5¾"

9¼"

3½"

BUTTOCK RAIL

3/8" PLY GUSSETS BOTH FACES

LIMBER HOLES PASS BILGE WATER

NOTCH FOR CHINE RAIL

33"

ONE PIECE BOTTOM

TAIL SHEER

1/8" X 2" X 2" ANGLE CLIPS BOLT TO RIB AND STRINGER

3/8" PLY SEAT

3¾"

TAIL FRAME

FRAME 1

34"

17¾"

5"

8½"

2¼"

3/8" BOTTOM LAPS 1/4" SIDE PLYWOOD AFT OF 5

31¼"

3/8" PLYWOOD TRANSOM BLANK

1 X 4" FRAMES

AFT DECK

31½"

1/4" PLY TAIL PANEL

21"

19¾"

24"

7½"

HEAVY OUTLINES ARE RIB FRAME BEFORE PLANKING

28½"

1"

TRANSOM LAYOUT AT STA. 0 (FLAT)

L. CAPITAN is framed on jig and receives its plywood bottom and sides while upside down. Use glue and screws to hold firmly.

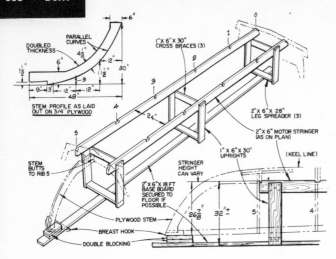

PARALLEL CURVES
DOUBLED THICKNESS
1"x6"x30" CROSS BRACES (3)
2"x6"x28" LEG SPREADER (3)
2"x6" MOTOR STRINGER (AS ON PLAN)
1"x6"x30" UPRIGHTS
STRINGER HEIGHT CAN VARY
(KEEL LINE)
STEM PROFILE AS LAID OUT ON 3/4" PLYWOOD
STEM BUTTS TO RIB 5
2"x6"x18 FT BASE BOARD SECURED TO FLOOR IF POSSIBLE
PLYWOOD STEM
BREAST HOOK
DOUBLE BLOCKING

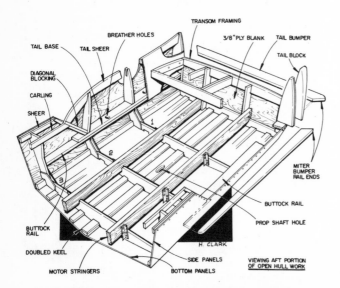

TRANSOM FRAMING
BREATHER HOLES
3/8"PLY BLANK
TAIL BUMPER
TAIL BASE
TAIL SHEER
TAIL BLOCK
DIAGONAL BLOCKING
CARLING
SHEER
MITER BUMPER RAIL ENDS
BUTTOCK RAIL
BUTTOCK RAIL
PROP SHAFT HOLE
DOUBLED KEEL
SIDE PANELS
VIEWING AFT PORTION OF OPEN HULL WORK
MOTOR STRINGERS
BOTTOM PANELS
H. CLARK

and fasten per the fastening schedule.

SPRAY RAILS: Spray rails are 1"x1¼" oak, and extend from the stem to the transom, covering the joint of the side and bottom planking. If preferred, these members may end aft of the front cockpit, as was done on the original prototype.

FINISHING HULL: The hull should be trimmed and sanded lightly. Screw holes and imperfections should be filled with a hard-setting wood putty.

FIBERGLASSING: If fiberglassing is desired, it should be accomplished at this time, or after the hull has been finished at the option of the builder. Glen L has available a fiberglass covering kit for the bottom only on the L. Capitan priced at $37.00 FOB, and one for the bottom, sides and transom, priced at $78.00 FOB. This includes the required resin, fiberglass cloth, squeegees, brushes, instructions, etc.

TAIL ASSEMBLY: The tail assembly is detailed in the drawings. Assembly is simple after the hull has been righted. The outer segments and inner segments of the tail section are covered with plywood. On the original, mahogany was used to enhance the appearance. At the junction of the tail with the side planking, a mahogany bumper rail is used that may also extend around the transom, as indicated.

FORWARD DECKING: The intermediate deck beam is installed at the position indicated and the deck batten and strongback installed. The decking is installed from

¼" plywood panels of two halves, to join over the strongback on the centerline.

MOTOR INSTALLATION: The motor installation will vary with the type of motor used. Dimensions given on the drawings are for general information only, and a full-size layout should be made to determine the exact position of all the components. Since such a process is slightly confusing to the amateur, a book is suggested; a text entitled "Inboard Motor Installations in Small Boats", available from Glen L. This book, priced at $6.00 postpaid, will cover most problems of inboard installations in craft of this type.

RUDDER: The rudder should be of a spade type, approximately 7"x1" in size. The strut is preferably a fixed-angle type held in place with four ⅜" bronze bolts.

SHAFT LOG: The shaft log is a self-adjusting, rubber-necked type of the proper angle to suit the installation. A catalog of underwater fittings can be obtained free of charge from Glen L upon request. This indicates all of the items required for the underwater propulsion system of the L. Capitan.

GASOLINE TANK: The gasoline tank shown in the details is a standard size, approximately 14 gallons. It should be securely chocked in position, connected to a flush deck fitting, and equipped with an overflow vent.

CONTROLS: The motor controls and steering, along with the instruments, should be brought to the front cockpit to suit the individual. The easiest type of steering to use on a boat of this type is push-pull type.

WINDSHIELD AND DECK FITTINGS: The windshield indicated is one of the plastic, curved types, 15" in height, and a minimum width of 72". The deck fittings can be varied to some extent. The lighting requirements should be checked with the Coast Guard or local governing bodies.

The foregoing has described an unusual type of boat. The details given in the plans, templates, and drawings, have been proven by many builders over a period of time. If you want a performing boat, build her like the plans. As far as needs are concerned, the original was powered with a Chevrolet V-8 conversion. The motor was of 1956 vintage, and the boat attained a speed of approximately 44 mph by water speedometer. •

PLAN SET AND FULL SIZE

patterns will greatly simplify construction of this boat, L. CAPITAN. Please consult your PLANS REFERENCE LISTING for the exact source and price. Refer to Plan Number 103.

RAKISH FINS are framed out as shown. Fit the plywood carefully for smooth finish.

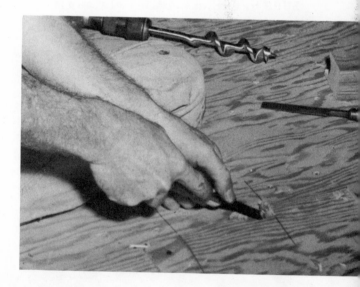

SHAFT HOLE is started with a wood chisel, as shown here, finished with a brace and bit.

WHEN SIDES AND BOTTOM are planked, hull is turned upright for interior and deck finishing.

Geronimo

By Glen L. Witt, N. A.

This extremely versatile 16-ft. runabout will take inboard power or single or twin outboards.

THE GERONIMO is a husky, open-type outboard runabout. You can mount back-to-back seats and use her for fishing or water skiing. With the removable seats pushed to one side you have a deep 5′ x 9′ cockpit, providing plenty of room for sleeping bags or skin diving equipment. You can build the Geronimo from plans and full size patterns or from the basic frame kit. The latter is easier and preferred by most. This unit consists of the transom, transom knee, stem, chine blocking, breasthook and each of the required frames for the construction of the boat, each cut and assembled from selected lumber.

Good materials should be used in building the Geronimo. Don't use interior plywood or inferior, punky, soft, or knotty lumber. Stick to bronze or hot dipped galvanized fastenings. Black iron fastenings will only rust out in short order and are not worth the effort required to put them in. Glue all of the joints with a hard setting type glue completely waterproofed, intended for exposure under marine conditions. Either the urea plastic resin type or the resorcinol may be used. The former is usually satisfactory if you are not attempting to glue to oak.

The Geronimo is constructed bottom side up on a building form or jig. This jig consists of two longitudinal members, spaced a convenient height above the floor, supported on legs, and level both lengthwise and athwartships. The entire structure should be securely anchored to prevent movement. The frames are mounted bottom side up on these longitudinals, accurately spaced, centered, and clamped rigidly in place. The heel of the stem is butted to the floor timber of the No. 5 frame and blocked securely in position.

BUILT by Ara Takouran, model shown is excellent performer. Photographed by Simon Nathan.

The transom angularity is controlled by the transom knee which is bolted on the keel. The height of the transom is jockeyed up and down so that the keel is a straight line in the after portion of the hull and braced in position.

The chine log is fitted into beveled notches in the frames so that the member will lie flat in the notches and not bear merely on one corner. After coating the notches and chine blocking with glue, fasten the chine log to the chine blocking with a single screw. Spring it about the hull, allowing it to flow about the frames in a smooth even curve. Use several more screws in the chine blocking and drive screws into each of the frames.

The sheer clamp is fitted similarly to the chine log except that it is put on in two laminations. Start the sheer clamp at the breasthook and spring it about the framework. The initial lamination is then coated with glue and the second layer applied. Use plenty of clamps to hold the laminations until the glue is set or use nails driven from the inside out.

All of the members, frames, stem, transom, keel, chine log, and sheer clamp must now be beveled so that the planking will lie flat or mate to them. A wood rasp is handy at the stem and for roughing in, but a plane, either power or hand, should be used in finishing up. Along the sheer, par-

ticularly up forward, you are going to remove considerable material. In fairing, always stand back every so often and sight along the lines of the hull. They are meant to be smooth, even flowing lines without humps or bumps. Careless fairing in the aft portion of the hull can result in irregular running surfaces that are detrimental to performance.

After all of the fairing has been done, the battens are accurately notched into the frames from the faired surfaces. After fitting and fastening the battens into their notches, be sure you cut limbers or drain holes on the outboard side of each of the longitudinals to enable all bilge water to drain aft and out through transom plugs.

The side planking is preferably full length plywood either ¼″ or ⅜″ in thickness. Lay the plywood directly against the hull side and roughly mark around the frame work extremities with a pencil. After the planking has been cut to shape, it is reapplied to the hull side and held with several locating screws or clamps for final fitting. The only area that must be closely fitted is that part of the panel that will join with the bottom planking in a butt joint along the chine.

Along the stem, sheer, and the balance of chine and transom, the panel may be left long for trimming to fit after it has been securely fastened in place. Before fastening

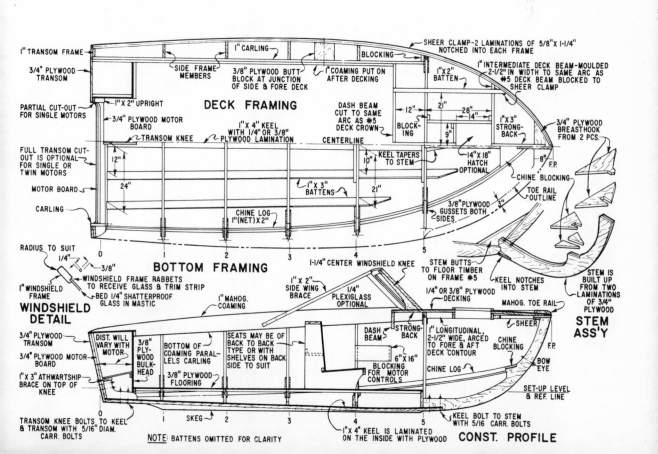

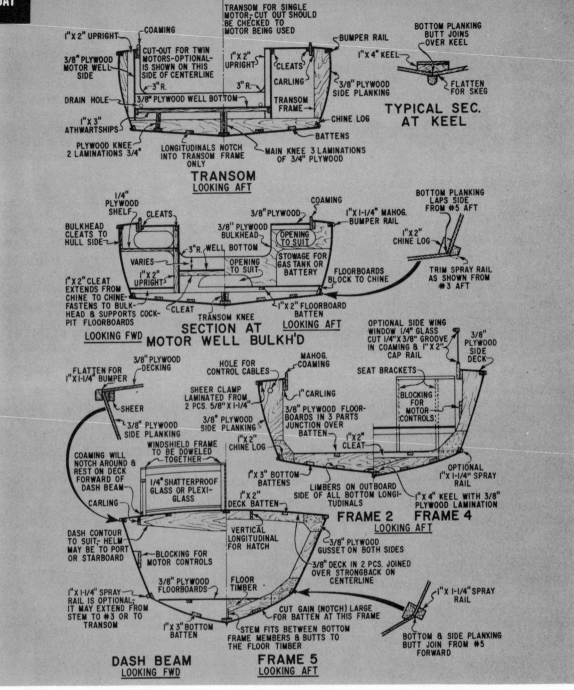

permanently into position, the fitted panels should be marked to another plywood sheet. Clean the chips and dust away and coat all of the mating surfaces for the side planking thoroughly with glue. Start driving the screws in the forward area along the chine working aft. Use a few clamps along the sheer and pull in the rolled portion or tumble home at the transom. After fastening, trim the overhang of the side panel along the chine, transom, and stem. Apply the opposite side planking in similar fashion, allowing it to overlap the initially applied panel at the stem.

The bottom planking is 3/8″ plywood fitted by aligning a straightedge of the panel along the center of the keel. Tempo-

rarily hold it in position in the after two thirds of the hull with several locating screws. Remove as much material as possible by rough cutting. Fitting the bottom planking to the side panel is rather difficult since the planking is fairly stiff. To loosen it up a bit, throw a couple of burlap sacks or rags across the offending area and pour on some boiling water. To fit the area along the chine that will butt join with the side planking, rub some chalk or crayola along the sharp edge of the side panel. Bump the bottom panel down on the coated edge to transfer the line to give a guide for rough cutting. You will still have to hand fit the panel progressively. Check the panel to the opposite side and scribe onto another

FRAMES are mounted on temporary jig. Hull is built upside down, righted for decking.

SHEER AND CHINE logs are installed after stem is firmly anchored to prevent warping.

ALL MEMBERS are faired so that the plywood skin will lie flat. Use glue and screws.

TURN HULL upright for topside work. Check with fairing stick, plane down high spots.

piece of plywood for the opposite half. Again, coat all of the mating surfaces with glue and fasten the panel with a couple of screws spotted along the keel. Force down the forward portion and fit into position, working as rapidly as you can. After application, trim the panel along the edges. The second half of the bottom is butted to the initially applied panel along the keel for most of the area. Up forward, however, along the stem, the second half bottom will lap the initially applied one.

The hull should be covered with fiberglass and resin to prevent the checking so common with fir plywood. You can obtain a complete covering kit for the bottom, sides, and transom for this boat from Glen

L Marine for $72.00 F.O.B. The hull should be righted and chocked in position so that it is again level both fore and aft and athwartships about the reference plane.

The carlings are the longitudinal members that form the extremities of the cockpit area. These extend from the transom to the No. 5 frame, fitting to the inside of the frame members. The carling, when viewed from above, is a straight line and it may be necessary to trim or remove some material from the frames to true in the member.

The intermediate deck beam is blocked to the sheer and the dash beam fitted between the carlings at the indicated point.

If you are going to handle an anchor line or mooring line, the opening deck hatch is

BILL OF MATERIALS

ITEM	MATERIAL	No. PCS.	SIZE
Frames	Oak, Mahogany, Spruce	50	Random Bd. Ft.
Frame Gussets	D.F. plywood, EXT Grade AB	1	3/8"x4'x4'
Transom, Stem, Breasthook, Chine Blocking & Knee	D.F. Plywood, EXT Grade AB	2	3/4"x4'x8'
Side Planking	D.F. Plywood, Marine Grade AA	2	3/8"x3'x18'
	D.F. Plywood, Marine Grade AA	2	3/8"x3'x16'
Bottom Planking	D.F. Plywood, Marine Grade AA	1	1"x4"x12'
Keel	Oak, Mahogany, Spruce	2	1" (net) x 2"x16'
Chine Log	Oak, Mahogany, Spruce	4	5/8"x1¼"x17'
Sheer Clamp	Oak, Mahogany, Spruce	2	1"x3"x12'
Battens, Bottom	Oak, Mahogany, Spruce	2	1"x3"x10'
Battens, Bottom	Oak, Mahogany, Spruce	1	1¼"x2"x10'
Skeg	Oak, Mahogany, Spruce	2	1"x1¼"x16'
Spray Rail (Optional)	Oak, Mahogany, Spruce	2	1"x1¼"x7'
Stem Cap Strip (Optional)	Oak, Mahogany, Spruce	2	1"x4"x12'
Carlings	Oak, Mahogany, Spruce	2	1"x7"x12'
Coamings	Oak, Mahogany, Spruce	1	1"x6"x5'
Intermediate Deck Beam	Oak, Mahogany, Spruce	1	1"x3"x7'
Hatch Framing	Oak, Mahogany, Spruce	2	1"x2"x4'
Deck Battens	Oak, Mahogany, Spruce	1	1"x3"x6'
Strongback	Oak, Mahogany, Spruce		
Decking	D.F. Plywood, EXT, Grade AB	2	3/8"x4'x8'
Floorboards, Seats, Bulkhead	D.F. Plywood, EXT, Grade AB	3	3/8"x4'x8'

FASTENINGS:

Bolts: Carriage with washers—Galvanized—six required—5/16" x 6"

Screws: Bronze or Hot Dipped Galvanized, Flathead, Wood Type.

1" #8	— 7 Gross
1¼" #8	— 1 Gross
2" #10	— 1 Gross

Nails: Annular Thread type, Monel or Bronze

3/4"	— 1 Lb.
1"	— 2 Lbs.
1¼"	— 3 Lbs.

Glue: Plastic Resin type "WELDWOOD" or comparable volume Resorcinol type—10 lbs.

desirable but may be eliminated if preferred. The hatch is formed by longitudinals arced to the fore and aft deck contour. The longitudinals are blocked to the intermediate and No. 5 deck beam. An athwartships beam is mounted between them. This framework forms the opening for the hatch. The hatch itself may be built up from 3/8" plywood with a frame of one-inch material completely around it. After the decking has been applied, a one-inch lip is fastened over the planking around the hatch opening. The hatch should be hinged to the foredeck and equipped with a standard hold down.

The strongback and battens are notched into each of the forward frames and fastened in place. The entire decking area must then be faired or trimmed so that the decking will lie flat and mate firmly to all members. This is a similar process to that accomplished for the side and bottom planking. The forward decking is put on in two parts, joined over the centerline of the strongback. Use a 4' x 8' sheet of exterior plywood, extending from the bow as far back as possible. At this point, a 3/8"

butt block is used to back the junction with the side decking. After coating the mating areas thoroughly with glue, the decking is nailed or screwed down.

The transom assembly incorporates a self bailing motor well. Any water splashing in over the transom cutout will immediately drain back out. You will probably have to adjust the clamping area, transom height cutout, fore and aft distance, and width to accommodate the particular motor that you intend to use.

The coaming parallels the carling member but projects above the deck. The forward portion fits to the windshield with a spline or doweled joint. Grooves should be provided in the windshield for the 1/4" safety glass. The center Vee part of the windshield is joined over a 1¼" knee. If preferred, the coaming and the windshield may be eliminated and the more conventional curved type windshield used.

The flooring is 3/8" plywood in three parts with the outer portions fitted around the gussets and blocked to the hull sides. The center section should be left removable for bilge inspection.

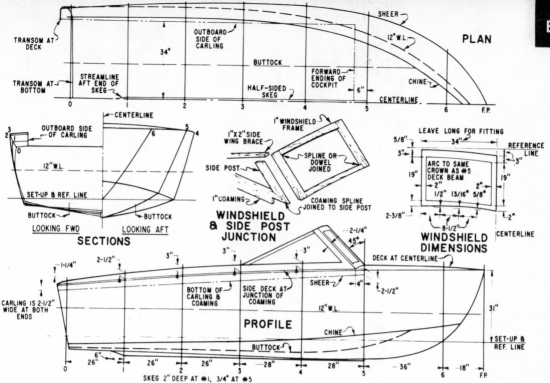

The Geronimo can handle any outboard motor, single or twins, to 90 hp. A good 40 hp motor will provide speeds of about 27 mph, plenty for most uses. A small inboard motor, not exceeding 600 lbs., could be used if it were stern mounted and connected to an inboard-outboard drive or a v-drive. If this is done, longitudinal 2″ x 4″ members should extend from the transom to as far forward as possible, blocked to the frames with 2″ x 3″ uprights. The motor is mounted on beds between longitudinals. •

PLAN SET AND FULL SIZE

patterns will greatly simplify construction of this boat, GERONIMO. Please consult your PLANS REFERENCE LISTING for the exact source and price. Refer to Plan Number 104.

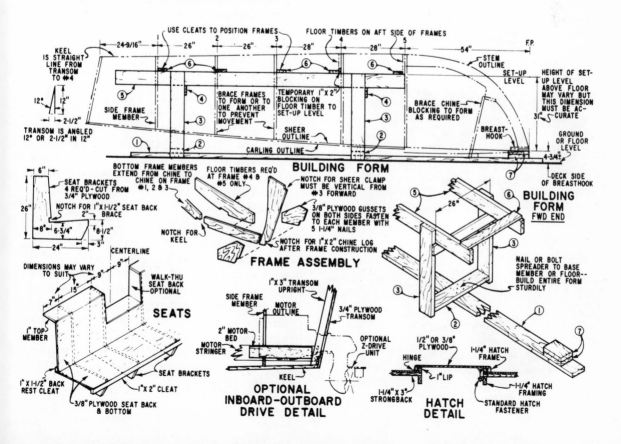

Float Boat

Swimmin'

Boatin'

Fishin'

Totin'

By C. C. Springfield

J. E. DAVIS, a Huntsville, Texas, insurance man, wanted to put a boat on the small lake behind his home. However, building a boat takes time and effort and he was reluctant to begin. Looking about, he saw four discarded inner tubes and some spare 1x4 lumber. He decided on a float.

The first float, about 3 ft. wide, looked like a ladder with inner tubes attached to frames at each corner. It floated like a chip but wasn't stable. Mr. Davis tried again, this time giving the "ladder" a wasp waist and a 5-ft. spread at each end. Loaded with two passengers, it performed well, but four made it sit down and become sluggish. To correct this, an additional piece of framework and two inner tubes were added. This worked like a charm.

Now Mr. Davis decided that he would like to go places on his float. He added a bracket and hung on a 3-hp motor. To really test it out, he brought the float boat to the Gulf of Mexico. It was so successful in calm and rough water and people were so interested that he applied for a patent and is now producing his creation for the market. If you can't wait to buy one, you can build your own easily by following the drawing on the opposite page. •

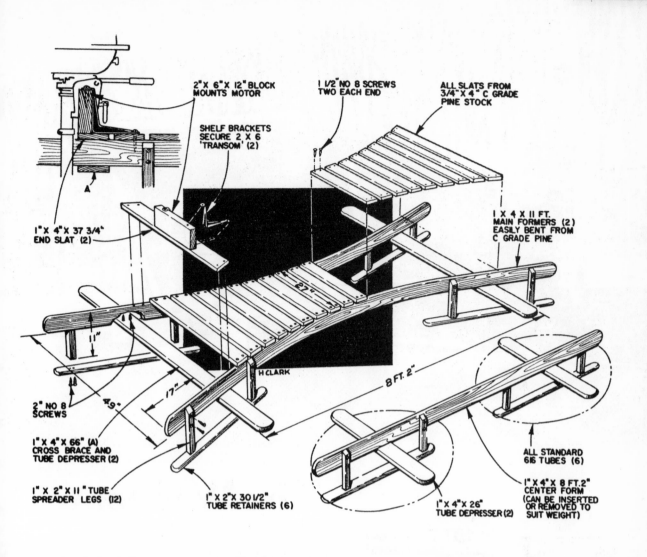

2"X 6"X 12" BLOCK MOUNTS MOTOR

1 1/2" NO 8 SCREWS TWO EACH END

ALL SLATS FROM 3/4"X 4" C GRADE PINE STOCK

SHELF BRACKETS SECURE 2 X 6 'TRANSOM' (2)

1"X 4"X 37 3/4" END SLAT (2)

1 X 4 X 11 FT. MAIN FORMERS (2) EASILY BENT FROM C GRADE PINE

27"

H CLARK

11"

2" NO 8 SCREWS

49°

17"

8 FT. 2"

1"X 4"X 66" (A) CROSS BRACE AND TUBE DEPRESSER (2)

1"X 2"X 11" TUBE SPREADER LEGS (12)

1"X 2"X 30 1/2" TUBE RETAINERS (6)

1"X 4"X 26" TUBE DEPRESSER (2)

ALL STANDARD 615 TUBES (6)

1"X 4"X 8 FT.2" CENTER FORM (CAN BE INSERTED OR REMOVED TO SUIT WEIGHT)

Center section fits between cross braces and slats, is held in place by two cleats.

The float boat weighs about 60 lbs. It's easily lifted to rack on car by one man.

The Widgeon

A nautical motif enlivens the design of this neat single-craft boathouse.

19 FT.

22 FT.

FLOOR PLAN

CONCRETE SLIPS

THIS is a single-craft onshore boathouse designed in the modern manner. The jaunty overhanging roof and portholes give it a distinctly nautical air. The single slip gives it ample room along either wall for storage space and work facilities. It's an ideal small boathouse for a community of modern summer homes. The bill of materials shown opposite lists all the supplies you'll need to build The Widgeon except interior finish.

The Widgeon and all other boathouses in this section were selected by the Outboard Boating Club of America. •

Rectangular plan incorporates single central slip with space on either side for storage, workbenches.

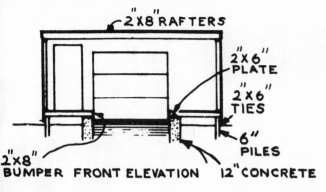

2"X8" RAFTERS

2"X6" PLATE

2"X6" TIES

6" PILES

2"X8" BUMPER FRONT ELEVATION

12" CONCRETE

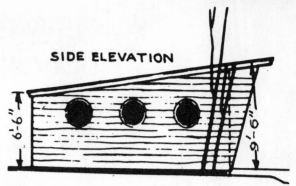

SIDE ELEVATION

6'-6"

9'-6"

BILL OF MATERIALS

Material	No. Units	Size
Piles	8	6" diameter
Ties	4	2"x6"—12'
Bumper board	4	2"x8"—12'
Floor joists	40	2"x6"—5'-6" long 16" o.c.
Plank flooring	250 sq. ft.	2½" thick
Side wall framing Studs	65	2"x4"—8' long 16" o.c.
Roof joists	20	2"x6"—20' long 16" o.c.
Roof sheathing & exposed soffit	550 sq. ft.	⅞" thick T. & G.

Material	No. Units	Size
Roll roofing	440 sq. ft.	2 layers.
Top & bottom plates & bracing wall (12" concrete water retaining)	242"x4"—12' long 44 lin. ft.	Depth depends on location (does not include extens on into water beyond house).
Siding	740 sq. ft.	Beveled lap siding
Trim	12	1"x8"—12'
Doors (All doors waterproof plywood)	2 1	8' wide x 7' high overhead door flush counterbalanced 3'x7' flush
Windows	6	2' diameter

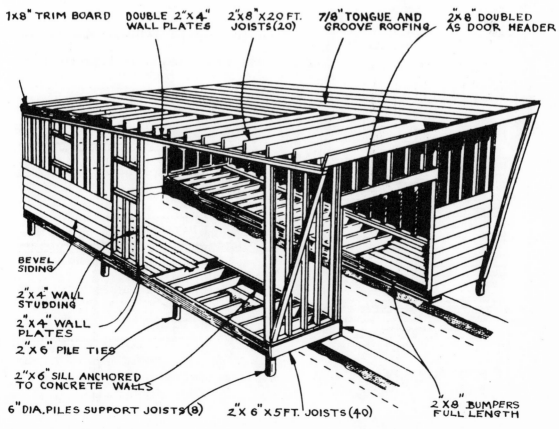

1x8" TRIM BOARD

DOUBLE 2"X4" WALL PLATES

2"X8"X20 FT. JOISTS (20)

⅞" TONGUE AND GROOVE ROOFING

2X8" DOUBLED AS DOOR HEADER

BEVEL SIDING

2"X4" WALL STUDDING

2"X4" WALL PLATES

2"X6" PILE TIES

2"X6" SILL ANCHORED TO CONCRETE WALLS

6" DIA. PILES SUPPORT JOISTS (8)

2"X 6"X 5FT. JOISTS (40)

2"X 8" BUMPERS FULL LENGTH

The Snipe

You can dock your boat on the first level and bask in the sun upstairs!

A SECOND floor containing a sundeck and a large room distinguishes this two-craft boathouse. No attempt has been made to divide the second-floor area, which can house a hobby room or contain dressing rooms for swimmers. Lines are simple to aid easy construction, yet have a very definite modern note. All materials necessary to building The Snipe are listed on the opposite page with the exception of those needed for the interior finish. ●

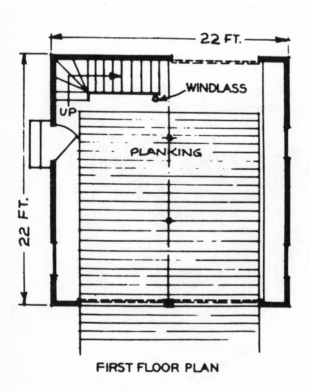

FIRST FLOOR PLAN

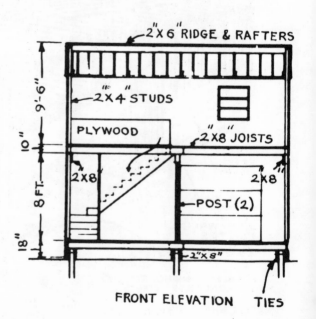

FRONT ELEVATION   TIES

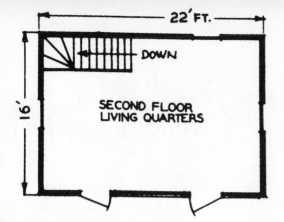

22' FT.

16'

SECOND FLOOR
LIVING QUARTERS

DOWN

BILL OF MATERIALS

Material	No. Units	Size
Piles	12	3" diameter
Ties	32	2"x8"-12' long
1st Floor joists	44	2"x8"-12' long 16" o.c.
1st Floor planking	500 sq. ft.	2½" thick boards
Side wall framing 1st & 2nd floors	45	2"x4"-12' long 16" o.c.
Studs	45	2"x4"-16' long 16" o.c.
	40	2"x4"-18' long 16" o.c.
	34	2"x4"-8' long 16" o.c.
	26	2"x4"-8' long 16" o.c.
Roof framing	40	
Ties	6	2"x4"—16' long
Sills and ridge	6	2"x6"—12' long
Top & bottom plates & bracing	28	2"x4"—12' long
Roof sheathing	360 sq. ft.	⅞" thick T. & G.
Roll roofing (roof & deck)	550 sq. ft.	2 layers of roll roofing
2nd floor joists	48	2"x8"—12' long
2nd floor planking	500 sq. ft.	2½" thick T. & G. (inc. deck)
2nd floor Beam	22' long.	2—2x10 spliced

Material	No. Units	Size
2nd floor Supporting columns	2	4" Lolly columns
2nd floor Deck open lattice flooring		1"x2" boards on 2x4 nailers to protect roofing—150 sq. ft.
Stair up	1	14 risers—10" wide treads. Use 2-2x12 stringers treads ¾"x10" solid.
Trim	10	1"x6"—12' long
	10	1½" wide moulding for trim at eaves
Siding	1400 sq. ft.	⅞" thick T. & G. Ran. width vert.
Doors, 1st floor (Flush waterproof plywood)	3	8' wide x 7' high —overhead doors —3 sections
	1	3'x7'
2nd floor	2	3'x7' (same as above)
Windows, 1st floor	3	3'x3' (3 lights)
2nd floor	3	3'x3' (3 lights)
	1	7'x3' (12 lights)
Awning		Provide awning

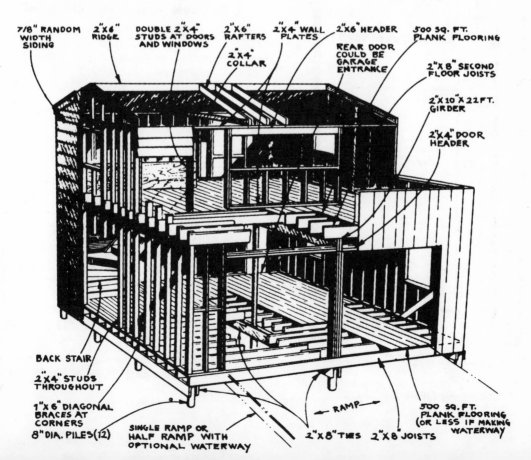

7/8" RANDOM WIDTH SIDING

2"X6" RIDGE

DOUBLE 2"X4" STUDS AT DOORS AND WINDOWS

2"X6" RAFTERS

2"X4" COLLAR

2"X4" WALL PLATES

2"X6" HEADER

REAR DOOR COULD BE GARAGE ENTRANCE

500 SQ. FT. PLANK FLOORING

2"X8" SECOND FLOOR JOISTS

2"X10"X 21FT. GIRDER

2"X4" DOOR HEADER

BACK STAIR

2"X4" STUDS THROUGHOUT

1"X6" DIAGONAL BRACES AT CORNERS

8"DIA. PILES(12)

SINGLE RAMP OR HALF RAMP WITH OPTIONAL WATERWAY

RAMP

2"X8" TIES

2"X8" JOISTS

500 SQ. FT. PLANK FLOORING (OR LESS IF MAKING WATERWAY

The Wood Duck

A flagpole and a modern window embellish this pile-based model.

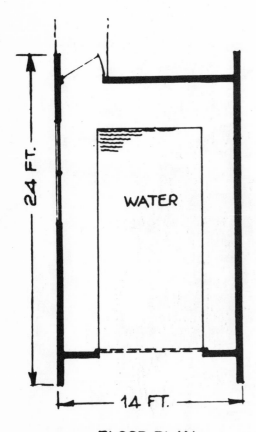

WATER

24 FT.

14 FT.

FLOOR PLAN

PILE type offshore boathouses are usually most successful in warm regions or sheltered bays where there is little danger of ice damage. However, the Wood Duck has been used even in the Far Northern states. It is a pile type which houses a single craft. Construction is extremely simple, but flagpole and large window give it a modern touch. Necessary materials are given opposite with the exception of supplies needed for interior finishing. Ample walkways around the slip provide for storage of boating equipment not in use. It is most suitable for use in shallow water. ●

Wide walkways around the slip and shore entrance at far left allow plenty of room for equipment.

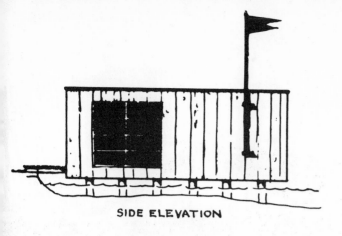

SIDE ELEVATION

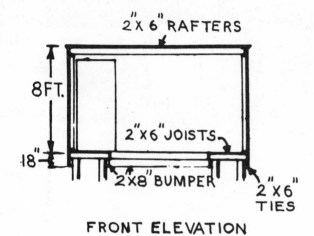

2 X 6" RAFTERS

8 FT.

2"X 6" JOISTS

18"

2"X 8" BUMPER

2"X 6" TIES

FRONT ELEVATION

BILL OF MATERIALS

Material	No. Units	Size
Piles	22	6" diameter
Ties	11	2"x6"—12' long
Beams	32	2"x6"— 3' long
	7	2"x6"— 4' long
Bumper board	5	2"x8"— 8' long
Floor planking	150 sq. ft.	2½" thick boards (does not include walk to shore)
Side wall framing		2"x4"— 8' long 16" o.c.
Studs	58	
Top & bottom plates	9	2"x4"—12' long
	3	2"x4"—14' long
Roof joists	19	2"x6"—14' long
Roof sheathing	340 sq. ft.	⅞" thick T. & G. Sheathing
Roll roofing	340 sq. ft.	2 layers roll roofing
Siding	620 sq. ft.	Waterproof plywood
Doors	1	8' wide x 7' high —water proof plywood overhead door with mechanism
	1	3' wide x 7' high —waterproof plywood flush door
Windows	2	3'-6" wide x 6'-6" high 4 lights high

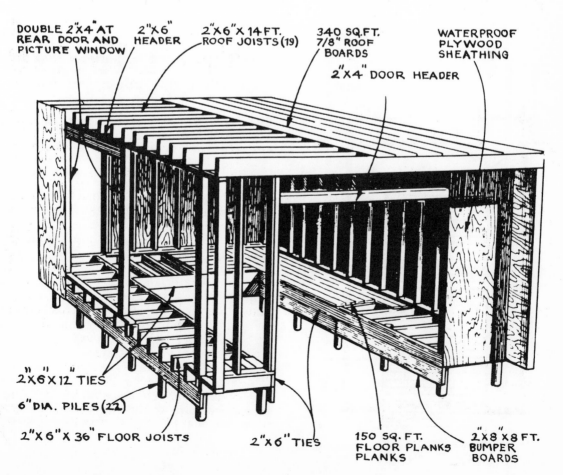

DOUBLE 2"X 4" AT REAR DOOR AND PICTURE WINDOW

2"X 6" HEADER

2"X 6"X 14 FT. ROOF JOISTS (19)

340 SQ. FT. 7/8" ROOF BOARDS

WATERPROOF PLYWOOD SHEATHING

2"X 4" DOOR HEADER

2"X 6"X 12" TIES

6" DIA. PILES (22)

2"X 6"X 36" FLOOR JOISTS

2"X 6" TIES

150 SQ. FT. FLOOR PLANKS PLANKS

2"X 8"X 8 FT. BUMPER BOARDS

The Bluegill

Because of this functional design, construction is easy and economical.

HERE is an easily constructed type of boathouse which makes maximum use of space, and provides perfect dry storage for a single boat. Its simple lines make it readily adaptable to the use of logs, stone, metal sheeting or the most easily obtainable materials in any locality. (Bill of materials shown opposite does not include interior wall finish.) This design also may be adapted for use of a connecting canal instead of the runway.

Remember that a boathouse can enhance or detract from your land and summer home. It need not be built of materials that exactly match your cabin but it should harmonize with cabin and grounds. ●

14 FT.

WINDLASS

20 FT.

FLOOR PLAN

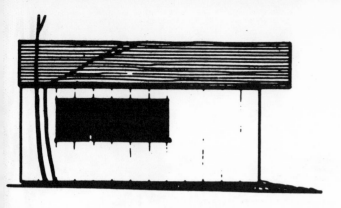

SIDE ELEVATION

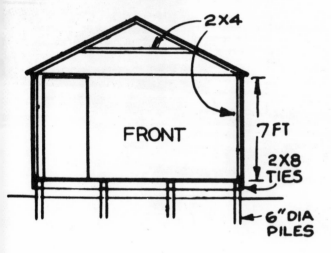

2X4

FRONT

7 FT

2X8 TIES

6" DIA PILES

BILL OF MATERIALS

Material	No. Units	Size
Piles	16	6" diameter
Ties	8	2"x8"—10' long
Beams	8	8" nominal—10' long
Floor planking	280 sq. ft.	2½" thick boards (does not include ramp)
Side wall framing Studs	52	2"x4"—7' long
Top and bottom plates	10	2"x4"—14' long
Roof truss	48	2"x6"—8' long
Roof sheathing	325 sq. ft.	⅞" thick Sheathing T. & G.
Roll roofing	325 sq. ft.	2 layers roll roofing with asphalt between layers and top surface
Siding	450 sq. ft.	⅞" thick Sheathing T. & G. siding vertical
Doors	1	8' wide x 7' high mechanical overhead plank door
	1	3'x7' plank door with hardware
Windows high	3	3'x3'—3 lights

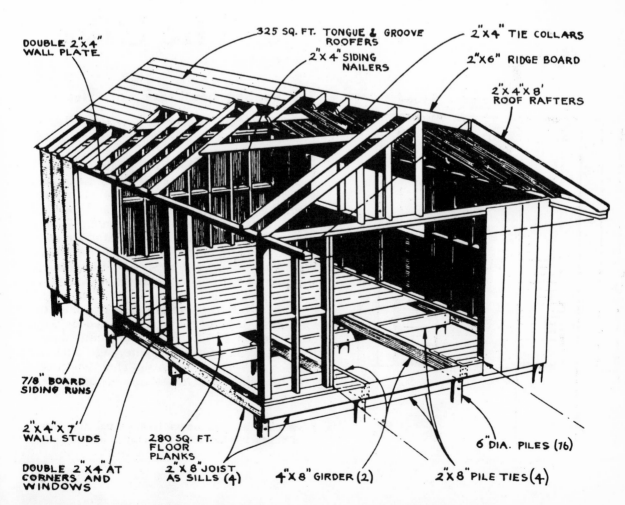

DOUBLE 2"X 4" WALL PLATE

325 SQ. FT. TONGUE & GROOVE ROOFERS

2"X 4" SIDING NAILERS

2"X4" TIE COLLARS

2"X6" RIDGE BOARD

2"X 4"X 8' ROOF RAFTERS

7/8" BOARD SIDING RUNS

2"X 4"X 7' WALL STUDS

DOUBLE 2"X 4" AT CORNERS AND WINDOWS

280 SQ. FT. FLOOR PLANKS

2"X 8"JOIST AS SILLS (4)

4"X 8" GIRDER (2)

2"X 8" PILE TIES (4)

6" DIA. PILES (16)

The Pike

The floating boathouse suits rivers where water levels vary seasonally.

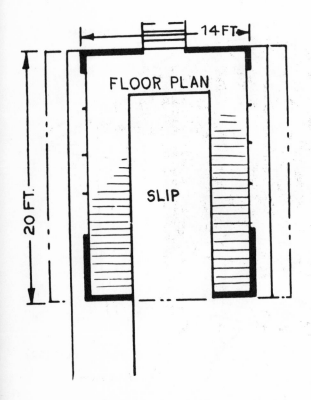

FLOOR PLAN

SLIP

14 FT.

20 FT.

HERE is a combination floating boat-house and dock particularly suitable for use on rivers where water levels vary with the seasons. Both dock and boat-house are supported on oil drums. The boathouse is well braced to withstand wave action without being thrown out of line. Walkways along either side of the single slip permit work to be done on your craft, and to facilitate loading. It's particularly appropriate for areas not subject to severe ice conditions. All materials needed in the construction of The Pike are included in the list given on the opposite page except for the interior wall finish. The structure may be enlarged to house another boat. ●

Floor plan is a rectangle with central slip. The high banks of windows give plenty of illumination.

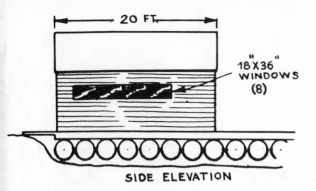

SIDE ELEVATION

18"X36" WINDOWS (8)

20 FT.

BILL OF MATERIALS

Material	No. Units	Size
Oil drums	26	55 gal. drums with 2-3/16"x1" iron strap to each drum
Floor joists	50	2"x6"—4'-8" long
	6	2"x6"—4'-0" long
Bumper board— inside & outside	11	2"x8"—12' long
Floor planking	300 sq. ft.	2½" thick boards
Framing	68	2"x4"—9' long 16" o.c.
Roof	38	2"x4"—12' long 16" o.c.
	17	2"x4"—20' long 16" o.c.
Top & bottom plates	14	2"x4"—12' long
Roof sheathing	460 sq. ft.	⅞" thick T. & G.
Roll roofing	460 sq. ft.	2 layers roll roofing
Siding	630 sq. ft.	⅞" thick beveled
Doors	1	7'x7' overhead— 3 section waterproof plywood door
	1	3'x7' flush waterproof plywood door
Windows	8	3' wide x 18" high

FRONT ELEVATION

20 FT.

4'-3"

8 FT.

8"

36"

2"X4

2"X8"

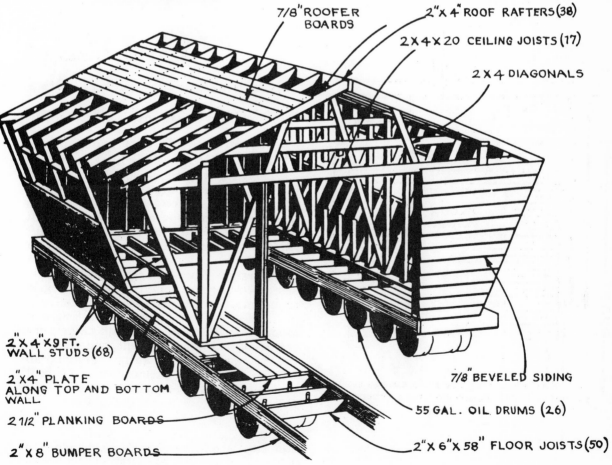

7/8" ROOFER BOARDS

2"X 4" ROOF RAFTERS (38)

2X4X20 CEILING JOISTS (17)

2 X 4 DIAGONALS

2"X 4"X 9 FT. WALL STUDS (68)

2"X 4" PLATE ALONG TOP AND BOTTOM WALL

2 1/2" PLANKING BOARDS

2"X 8" BUMPER BOARDS

7/8" BEVELED SIDING

55 GAL. OIL DRUMS (26)

2"X 6"X 58" FLOOR JOISTS (50)

The Bass

This is a handsome structure with a wide ramp and space for three boats.

THE BASS—A well-lighted shelter for three boats, whose low lines provide for complete harmony with the surrounding shoreline. Space is ample to provide dead storage for one broad-beamed craft such as a sailboat, and two smaller craft. Multiple windows at the roof line also aid ventilation.

The ramp extends the full width of the structure to permit any of the three boats to be moved. Extension of the roof line protects the doors, and adds a touch of modern to the design. Posts divide the storage area into three parts, and eliminate the necessity for lengthy or elaborate trusses to support the roof. Can be built of a variety of materials. ●

30 FT.

24 FT.

FLOOR
PLANKING

PLAN

RAMP

Posts divide floor plan into three storage sections, support roof and separate the three overhead doors.

SIDE ELEVATION

2X6 RAFTERS

4 X10

2X8

4X8

2 X10

8" DIA. PILES

FRONT ELEVATION

BILL OF MATERIALS

Material	No. Units	Size
Piles	16	8" diameter
Ties	8	2"x10"-10' long
	4	2"x10"-12' long
Beams	16	4"x8"-12' long
	4	2"x8"-12' long
Floor planking	720 sq. ft. 2½" thick (does not include ramp)	
Framing studs	32	2"x4"-12' long
	27	2"x4"-7' long
	14	2"x4"-8' long
top & bottom plates	26	2"x4"-12' long
Roof framing girders	4	4"x10"-12' long
beams	8	2"x8"-10' long
	4	2"x8"-12' long
joists	48	2"x6"-10' long
Roof sheathing	720 sq. ft. ⅞" thick sheathing T. & G.	
Roll roofing	720 sq. ft. 2 layers roll roofing with asphalt between layers and on top surface	
Siding	850 sq. ft. ¾" thick waterproof plywood	
Doors	2	7' wide x 7' high —3 section flush waterproof plywood overhead door, provide hardware
	1	3'x7' flush plywood door provide hardware
Windows	9	3' wide x 2' high —1 light

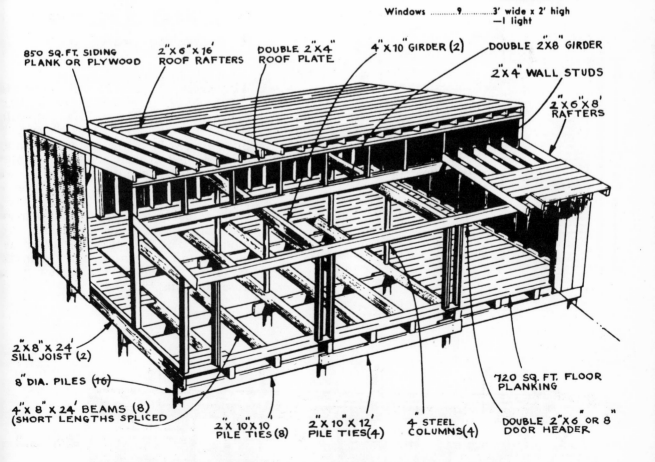

850 SQ. FT. SIDING PLANK OR PLYWOOD

2"X6"X16' ROOF RAFTERS

DOUBLE 2"X4" ROOF PLATE

4"X10" GIRDER (2)

DOUBLE 2"X8" GIRDER

2"X4" WALL STUDS

2"X6"X8' RAFTERS

2"X8"X24' SILL JOIST (2)

8" DIA. PILES (16)

4"X8"X24' BEAMS (8) (SHORT LENGTHS SPLICED

2"X10"X10' PILE TIES (8)

2"X10"X12' PILE TIES (4)

4" STEEL COLUMNS (4)

720 SQ. FT. FLOOR PLANKING

DOUBLE 2"X6" OR 8" DOOR HEADER

END VIEW

4 X 10'

A

'U' BOLTS

The Tidewater

BILL OF MATERIALS

Material	Unit	Size
Floats	4	6' wide x 8' long with 2 4" x 10" anchor beams
Beams	2	4"x12"—18' long
Beams	2	4"x12"—20' long
Beam	1	4"x12"—8' long
Beam splice plates	4	2"x12"—3' long
Floor joists	21	2"x8"—8' long
Floor planking	300 sq.ft.	2½" boards
Posts	8	8" diameter—3' long
Shoe plate	1	2' wide x 8' long x ⅛" thick
Cable anchor eyes	2	
Bumper plates	5	2"x10"—20' long
Steel angles	4	3"x3"x¼"—12" long
Beam anchor bolts	64	U-anchor bolts ½" diameter for anchorage to floats

This floating dock adapts to fluctuating water levels.

WHERE VARIATIONS in water level occur, a floating dock of the pontoon type such as The Tidewater should be used. If desired, it may be built in two sections as an L-shaped or T-shaped dock. Once water-soaked such pontoons should require no care throughout the season. This type of support distributes the weight, and is well adapted to carrying heavy loads. Snubbing posts are provided for mooring. The bill of materials at left includes all necessary units with the exception of cables for anchorage or miscellaneous bolts. •

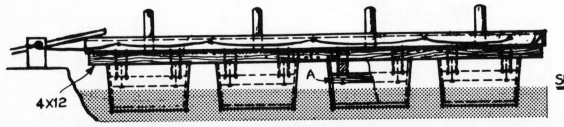

4 X 12

A

SIDE VIEW

The Cozy Cove

BILL OF MATERIALS

Material	Unit	Size
Piles	12	6" diameter
Horizontal ties	14	2"x8"—10' long
Floor beams	6	2"x8'—18' long
Floor beams	3	2"x8"—12' long
Floor planking	400 sq.ft.	1" thick

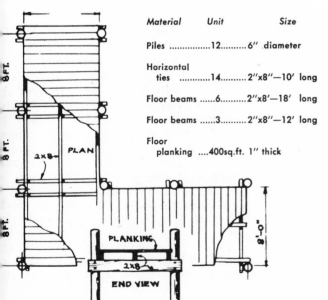

If water levels seldom change, use a pile-driven installation.

FOR LAKES where water levels are almost constant, The Cozy Cove will be a most suitable installation. It is an L-shaped dock mounted on driven piles and is to be used as a semi-permanent construction. The L-shape provides some shelter for moored boats in the event of storms. With piling driven to a solid footing there is little danger of such a dock being moved or damaged by heavy weather. It may also be built as a straight extension from the shore or in T-shape. The bill at left lists all items except bolts. •

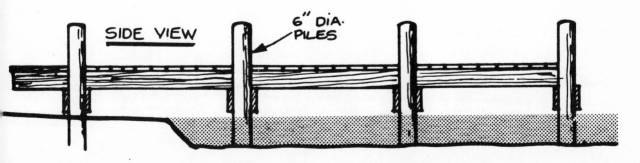

DOCKS, RAMPS AND STORAGE SHELTERS

Proper access and a secure mooring are necessities for any boat.

DID YOU ever return from a weekend cruise and find that your mooring buoy had sunk? Have you ever tried to launch your boat from a trailer and had the entire rig bog down in mud before you could reach the water's edge? Have you spent time and money on floats, or in building a pier, and found that the float's bouyancy was so poor that the float was dangerous to use or the pier disintegrated due to tide, current, freezing or banging?

Have you wanted to construct a floating wharf or a floating boat house and not been sure how to figure flotation needs or the more desirable materials to use? The following ideas should help clarify some of your problems concerning improvement of your own, your club or municipal boating facilities.

LAUNCHING RAMPS

• **Permanent launching ramps** are usually community or club projects. The Outboard Boating Club of America, 307 No. Michigan Avenue, Chicago 1, Illinois, offers a free brochure titled *Boating Facili-*

ties For Your Community which relates the fictionalized case history of how a boat club was able to bring improved boating facilities to its community. The booklet is based on the experiences of many clubs in many communities and is intended as a guide to establish a program to improve boat launching and mooring facilities in any town.

Included is a complete blueprint explaining how a group can promote a drive to open new boating waters.

• **Permanent** launching ramps can be constructed of poured concrete, pre-cast concrete, asphalt, cinders, gravel, or sections of surplus metal aircraft landing strips.

• **Precast concrete** ramps are generally lower in construction costs than are poured concrete ramps. One recommended method is to build rectangular forms of plywood, four inches high, 14 inches wide and 10 feet long. The form is placed on a section

of corrugated metal, cut slightly larger than the form itself. When the poured concrete hardens, edges of the metal are hammered down smoothly over the concrete slab and the slabs are placed metal side up. The corrugation offers traction for car wheels. The area for the ramp is graded, and if muddy, is covered with a gravel surface. The pre-formed planks are laid in position with a mixture of sand and gravel filling the space approximately four inches in width between each slab.

• **Asphalt ramps** are popular in locations where the bank's soil is not subject to washouts and where ice and frost are not common.

• **The ramps least expensive** to build are those with gravel, cinders or crushed shell surfaces. These are adequate in locations where wave action, current and tides do not create an erosion problem.

• **Though concrete ramps** of the poured type are expensive, modern methods permit pouring concrete under water without the requirement of expensive-to-construct temporary coffer dams. Maintenance is usually modest. In areas where marine growth builds up rapidly, non-skid surfacing of poured concrete is important. The simplest solution is to draw a garden rake across the ramp surface, before the concrete has set, creating deep traction grooves.

HOW TO CALCULATE FLOTATION

• **Determine in advance** how much weight each section of floating structure will be expected to support, then add to this weight the total weight of the structure to be supported above water level. Then, figure the buoyancy per cubic foot of the type flotation material to be used. A cubic foot of air can support approximately 62 pounds, less the weight of its container. To simplify things, the weight of the containers to be used as flotation

Small boats can be rolled onto beach for protection by using a pair of inflatable rollers.

Some methods of securing floating structures. You'll think of other ways to fit the situation.

Courtesy of Dow Chemical Corp.

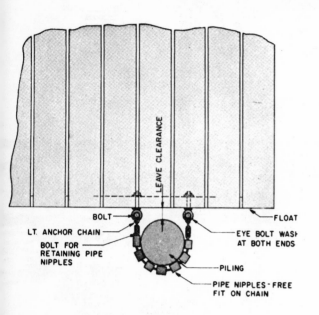

TOP VIEW

TIDAL FLOAT TO PILING

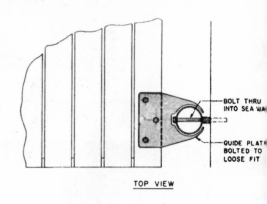

TOP VIEW

TIDAL FLOAT TO SEA WALL

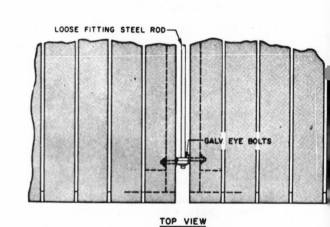

TOP VIEW

FLOAT TO FLOAT

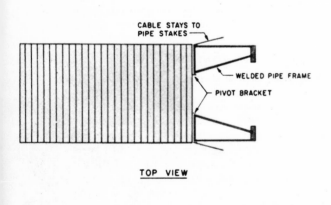

TOP VIEW

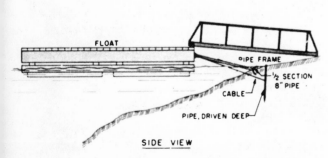

SIDE VIEW

FLOAT TO BEACH

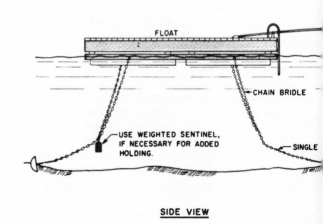

SIDE VIEW

FLOAT ANCHORING

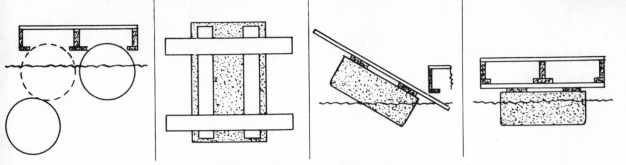

Left to right: Four stages in replacing 55-gallon drums under a float with Styrofoam flotation.

Courtesy of Dow Chemical Corp.

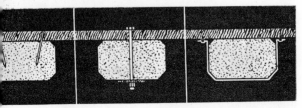

Three means of attaching Styrofoam logs to the wood in a float: dowels, bolts or metal straps.

Homemade, crank-type lift in which rope slings wind up on rotating pipes to raise small boat.

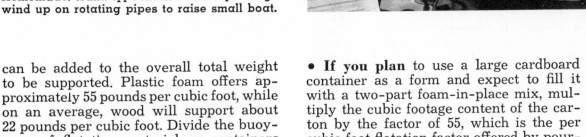

can be added to the overall total weight to be supported. Plastic foam offers approximately 55 pounds per cubic foot, while on an average, wood will support about 22 pounds per cubic foot. Divide the buoyancy of flotation material or containers into the total weight to be supported and this will offer the minimum cubic footage of flotation material required. It is well to add to this about a 30% safety factor.

• **For stability** when building floats, keep in mind that long, thin, wide shapes are preferred to short, narrow, high shapes.

• **A cubic foot** contains 1,728 cubic inches. Where drums are to be used, one simple way of determining the volume of the container is to fill it with water. If you use a bucket, weigh the bucket and subtract this weight from the weight of the filled bucket which gives the weight of the water. You can use an ordinary bathroom scale for this purpose. You need not fill the bucket to the same level if you weigh each load and keep a record. When the container has been topped off, divide the total weight of the water required to fill it by 62, the weight per cubic foot of water. This figure, less the weight of the container, will be the total number of pounds of buoyancy afforded by the air-filled container.

• **If you plan** to use a large cardboard container as a form and expect to fill it with a two-part foam-in-place mix, multiply the cubic footage content of the carton by the factor of 55, which is the per cubic foot flotation factor offered by pour-in-place foam.

EXPANDED POLYSTYRENE

• **Expanded polystyrene**, formed in rigid foamed plastic blocks or logs, consists of millions of tiny non-interconnected gas-filled cells which act as independent buoyancy chambers. One commonly used rigid foam is Styrofoam. One cubic foot of Styrofoam weighs approximately two pounds so that this advertised flotation of 55 pounds includes approximately a 5-pound safety margin. The material is resistant to destruction by marine growth and organisms, it is easy to work with conventional tools, offers low maintenance cost, and its buoyancy is reduced by punctures or damage only to the extent of the volume affected. It does have certain limitations. Though it is unaffected by temperature, solvents such as gasoline and oils will damage it. In areas infested with muskrats or otter it is recommended that Styrofoam logs used for flotation be encased in galvanized wire mesh of ¼″ to ⅜″ size to prevent

Crank-up cradle raises boat to shelter in this dockside unit made by the Sagen Boat Hoist Co.

Kleeco floating steel boathouse is sold in 20- 30- or 40-foot lengths for boats up to 38 feet.

water animals from chewing out spaces for nests.

• **When used where ice floes** or heaving ice may be encountered, or to protect against mechanical damage of boats or driftwood striking the floating logs, skirt boards are recommended on Styrofoam.

• **If there is danger** of fuel mixture floating on the water's surface, somewhat more expensive Tyrilfoam buoyancy billets are recommended, or Styrofoam blocks may be coated with epoxy, not polyester resin, as a protection.

INSTALLATION OF RIGID FOAM PLASTIC

• **Four methods** are commonly used to fasten Styrofoam logs to the underwide of a floating structure: dowels, bolts, bands and wood planking.

• **The dowel method** calls for ¾-inch maple dowels treated with a preservative, preferably a water-repellant type containing pentachlorophenol. The dowels should be pointed and driven at an acute angle approximately ¾ of the way through the foam log but never all the way through. Secure the dowels with galvanized 6d nails. To bolt Styrofoam in place the foam logs should have a backing board approximately 6 inches square by ½ inch thick to prevent the bolt head or the nut from pulling through the foam. Boards running the entire length of the underside of the Styrofoam, drilled and bolted are satisfactory. The bolts should be aluminum, brass, galvanized or plastic coated.

• **Stainless steel** or copper straps at least

2 inches wide can be drawn around the logs, the straps nailed to the undercarriage of the floating structure with hot-dipped galvanized, bronze or cadmium-plated annular boat nails. The most satisfactory method is to bolt the blocks in place. Wood used for the floating structure should be of a type resistant to decay and should be preservative-treated with permanent non-leaching preservative. Submerged wooden portions of framing, such as skirt boards, should be treated against marine borer attack in the same manner as a wood boat.

MARINE ORGANISMS

• **Foam flotation,** metal air containers, precast cement air containers, steel or aluminum pontoons, in fact all submerged floating dock materials will be subject to a build-up of marine grass, marine crustaceans and other organisms in the same amount as any submerged materials will be in the waters where the floats are anchored. Accumulated fouling will cause some settling due to added weight, but, in general, the initial growths that attach themselves will die as added growth occurs and the material will slough off periodically and will seldom result in growth totaling more than 5 pounds per square foot. An occasional scraping with a blunt instrument will remove growth if no antifouling finish has been used, or if it has lost its effectiveness.

PRE-FAB DOCKS AND FLOATS

• **Many of the manufacturers** of the increasingly popular float boats or pontoon boats, sell pontoons fitted with brackets topside so that they form excellent dock floats requiring a minimum of building problems. •

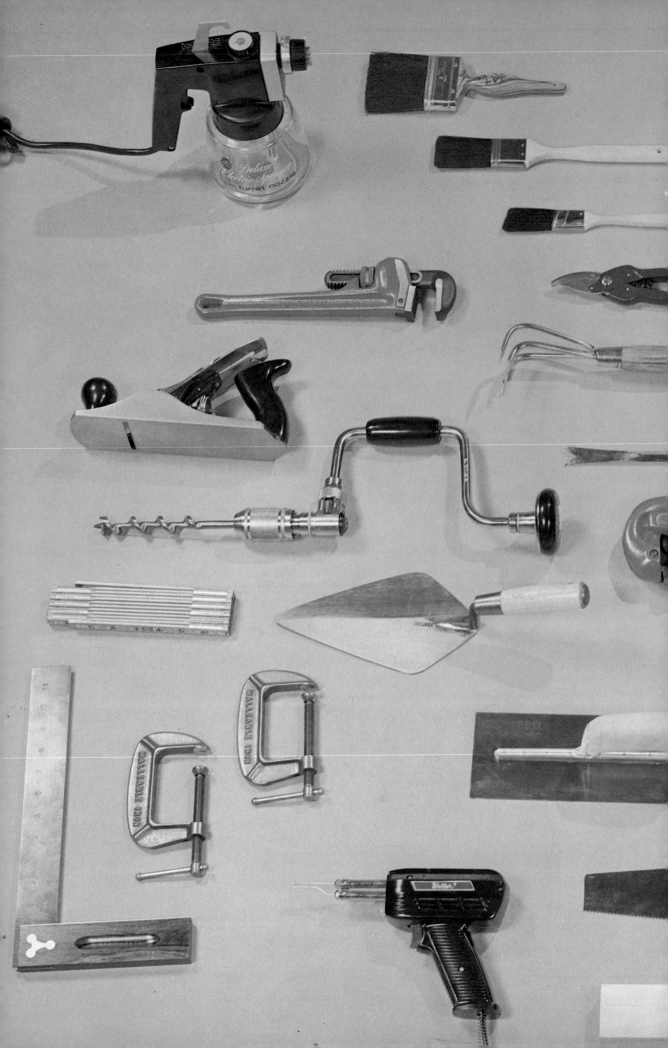